Noah Webster

A Man Who Loved Words

Elaine Cunningham

A B... Pensacola, FL 32523-9100
a ministry of PENSACOLA CHRISTIAN COLLEGE

Noah Webster: A Man Who Loved Words

Staff Credits
Cover Design: Steven Haught
Illustrator: David Apling

A Beka Book, a Christian textbook ministry of Pensacola Christian College, is designed to meet the need for Christian textbooks and teaching aids. The purpose of this publishing ministry is to help Christian schools reach children and young people for the Lord and train them in the Christian way of life.

Cataloging Data

Cunningham, Elaine.
    Noah Webster: a man who loved words / by
   Elaine Cunningham; illustrated by David Apling.
        180 p.: ill.; 23 cm. [A Beka Book Reading
        Program]
        1. Reading. 2. Readers I. Apling, David.
II. Series

Library of Congress: PE1119 .C86 N63 1998
Dewey System: 428.6

Contents

Introduction

This is a story based on events in the life of Noah Webster. I have tried to be as accurate as possible with dates and known information. Most episodes in Noah's life, from college years on, were documented by his diary and other original sources.

Little is known of Noah's childhood. I wrote the earlier chapters as it could have happened in the life of a boy who lived in the 1700s.

Many thanks are due to Sally P. Whipple, director of education of the Noah Webster Foundation in Hartford, Connecticut, who gave me much helpful information along with photos of the Noah Webster House, maps, diagrams, and brochures. She also read the manuscript and made suggestions regarding colonial terminology and facts about the Webster family.

Librarians from several cities have assisted in finding information. I am also grateful to my husband, Cloyce, who supported me in many ways during the writing of this book.

If, in some small way, I have helped today's children to know more about this great American patriot, Noah Webster, it is worth all the hours of research and writing that I have done.

Elaine Cunningham

1
The Boy Who Wanted to Read

January 1764

An icy blast of wind blew fiercely down the great chimney of the old farmhouse near Hartford, Connecticut. It rattled the loosely fitted windows in the kitchen. Drying herbs, hanging from the ceiling, swayed in the breeze. A candle in its sconce flickered in a draft.

On the worktable beneath the window sat a brown crock filled with yellow cornmeal. Two eggs lay beside a bowl of butter. From the fireplace came the delicious smell of roasting meat. In the center of the room a round table, surrounded by six ladder-back chairs, was set with only a pewter bowl and pitcher.

Mercy Webster, short and slim, stood beside the window, a paper-covered booklet in her hand. With dark brown hair pinned neatly behind her head, and rosy cheeks, she looked more like one of the girls than a thirty-seven-year-old mother of five. Her short gown and petticoat were covered by a dark blue linen apron.

Five-year-old Noah, wearing a brown wool shirt and tan breeches, stood beside his mother. He was tall for his age, with red hair and fair skin. Munching on a piece of dried apple, he looked up at her. "What do you have, Ma?" he asked.

"Your Pa bought us a new almanack today," she said, pushing a stray hair from her face.

Noah's gray eyes sparkled as he eagerly reached for the booklet. "Let me see it, Ma, please."

"If your hands are clean, you may sit on the bench and look at it." Mistress Webster looked out the window. "Your sisters and brother will be home from school soon, so we need to get busy."

She handed the booklet to Noah. Looking at the front cover, he asked, "What does A-L-M-A-N-A-C-K say, Ma?"

"It says almanack."

"What does that mean?"

"It's a calendar, and it tells about the weather and the stars. Doctor Nathaniel Ames prints one every year."

Noah turned the pages. "I wish I could read it. What does it say, Ma? Please teach me to read."

With a puzzled expression, Mistress Webster looked at her impatient son. "Why does a little shaver like you want to know every-thing? You'll soon be going to school."

"I like to hear the words. I want to learn things. Read it to me, Ma, please," he begged, as he tugged at her apron strings.

"Well, let me see. On this page it says, ' They who do not work must not eat.' " Glancing at Noah, she said, "That's a proverb." She smiled. "And if I don't get to work soon, *we* won't eat. That reminds me of another proverb I learned when I was a little girl. 'The sleeping fox catches no poultry.' "

Noah was quiet for a minute, thinking about the proverb. In his imagination he could see a fox asleep, with chickens peeking around a corner. He burst into cheerful laughter when he understood what it meant. "Tell me some more," he pleaded.

Mother continued, "This next page has an article telling about Benjamin Franklin's new invention called a lightning rod."

"What's a lightning rod?" Noah asked.

Mother stopped reading and walked across the kitchen to tend the meat roasting in the huge fireplace. "It protects buildings so they don't burn down if lightning strikes." She called to Noah, "Now you come here, son. Please turn the spit so this roast doesn't burn. I must get a pan of corn bread baked before your sisters and Abram get home from school. Pa will be coming in from the barn, too."

Carefully putting a piece of string through the pages of the almanack, Noah hung the small book on a nail behind the door. He stepped over the sand that covered the floor in front of the fireplace. The sand was there to catch grease from the roasting meat.

Noah was just tall enough to reach the handle that turned the sharp iron rod called a spit. The fat in the meat sputtered and crackled. Noah sniffed the air. "It smells good." The beef roast, with the spit in its middle, was brown and juicy. Drippings plopped into a pan underneath and splashed over onto the sand.

Going as close to the glowing flame as he dared, Noah stared into the fire. *What makes brown wood turn to red?* he wondered. *And why are the ashes gray? There are so many things to think about.* He felt his cheeks. Hot. The heat from the fireplace made them burn. His arms felt warm too. Switching arms, Noah wondered if he was cooking, along with the meat.

As he turned the spit, Noah could see the pots and pans hanging from a crane in the fireplace. A big kettle for boiling water hung beside smaller ones for cooking vegetables and meat. The warming pan that Ma used to heat the beds sat beside the bellows. When he saw the churn sitting next to the fireplace, Noah suddenly remembered that he was hungry. *I'd like some butter on homemade bread right now. With some of Ma's applesauce.*

Noah looked out the window. It was getting dark, but he could still see the drifts of snow between the barn and the well. Snow came almost up to the window sills. Icicles hung from the eaves. *I wonder what makes ice?*

Noah thought. *Why is the snow white? There are so many things to learn. It's such a big world, and I want to read about it.* His thoughts were interrupted by the stomping of feet outside the door. Noah's sisters, fourteen-year-old Mercy (named after her mother) and seven-year-old Jerusha, came rushing inside, brushing snow off their coat sleeves.

"Guess what happened to Abram today," Jerusha said, her dark eyes flashing as she smoothed her tumbled brown hair. Ma looked up from the bowl of dough.

Noah stopped turning the spit. "What happened?" he asked.

"The schoolmaster hit him with a stick because he didn't know the answer to a question."

"Where is Abram now?" Mother said, brushing cornmeal flour off her arms.

"He went out to the barn. He wanted to see Pa."

"Well, Pa will talk to him about it. You girls get your things off. Jerusha, you may set the table while Mercy goes to get Baby Charles. I hear him crying in the parlor." Mercy went to get the baby. Her light brown hair, hanging nearly to her waist, swung from side to side as she hurried out of the room.

Noah thought about school. *I want to go and learn to read but I don't want to get hit by*

*the schoolmaster. When I go to school, I'll know
all the answers to all the questions,* he decided.
*If I'm a teacher some day, I'll never use the stick
on any of my pupils.*

With much stamping of feet, Pa and Abram
came into the kitchen. Noah Webster, Senior,
tall and sturdy, came over and stooped down to
Noah's level. "How is my little namesake today?" he asked. Noah smelled hay and cows
and other barnyard smells as Pa came near.
"I'm helping Ma with the roast," he said. "It's
almost ready for supper."

"It smells mighty good," Pa said, as he
headed for the table.

Twelve-year-old Abraham, better known as
Abram, sat down beside Pa. He was tall and
slim, and his brown hair matched his brown
eyes. His ambition was to be a farmer when he
grew up.

Mercy came into the kitchen carrying
Charles, who would be two years old the next
September. A chubby baby, he was an armful
for his big sister. Jerusha and Ma joined Noah
and the others at the table. Pa asked the bless-
ing. The wind whistled around the corners of
the old farmhouse, but inside the kitchen a
roaring fire kept the Websters snug and warm.

Winter passed. Spring arrived with lilacs
and apple trees in bloom. Birds built nests,
and baby animals were born. On a clear, spar-

kling spring day, fresh with new leaves and the song of birds, Mother read the almanack verse for the month of May.

"Increasing heat and blooming trees, delight mankind as well as bees."

How do bees make honey? Noah wondered. Watching them fly from one blossom to another, he figured it out. *It must have something to do with the flowers. There are so many things to learn. I wish I knew how to read.*

Long, hot summer days came. Helping in the vegetable garden, Noah weeded the long rows. He picked peas and lettuce. Later in the summer, he dug carrots. When the work was done, he took a stick and drew pictures and letters in the dirt, erasing them with his bare feet. Some days Noah pretended that he was a schoolteacher. Baby Charles and Rhoda the dog were his pupils. Other times he was a farmer. Or a weaver. With his lively imagination, the hours passed quickly.

At the close of each day, after family prayer and Bible reading, Noah climbed the steep wooden stairs to the south chamber and crawled into bed with his big brother Abram.

Early one morning, Pa called to Noah, "Do you want to go along with me to the black-smith? Betsey needs new shoes."

Noah ran quickly to Pa. He was lifted up and settled behind Pa's saddle on the bare back of old Betsey. Putting his arms around Pa's waist, Noah hung on tightly as the horse trotted down the ridge.

"It won't be long before you go to school, will it, Noah?" Pa said. "You're growing up fast."

"I can't wait to learn to read," Noah replied.

When they stopped at the blacksmith's shed, Noah slid down from the horse. Taking Noah's hand, Pa walked toward a large, dark-haired man with bulging arm muscles standing over another man who sat on a stool. As they came closer, Noah saw the blacksmith pull out the man's tooth with iron pincers.

"Does that hurt?" Noah whispered to Pa.

"I'm sure it does," Pa answered. "But there's no other way to stop an aching tooth."

The blacksmith, Ebenezer Crosby, walked toward Noah and his father.

"What can I do for you, Mr. Webster? And who do you have with you today?"

"This is my son, Noah, Junior," Pa said. "We've brought Betsey. She needs shoes."

"Bring her here. We'll see what we can do."

Noah watched as Pa led Betsey to the blacksmith. Mr. Crosby stood at the horse's left shoulder, facing the same direction that Betsey faced. He gently tapped the back of the horse's left foreleg. Betsey raised her foot. The smith placed Betsey's hoof on a wooden block.

Standing in front of Betsey, his knees slightly bent, the blacksmith put the horse's foreleg between his knees. With a pair of trimming pliers, he snipped off the bent ends of the nails which held the old shoe on. He pried the horseshoe off.

"Young man, why don't you walk Betsey back and forth a bit," the smith said. "We'll see how even she walks."

Feeling very proud, Noah took the bridle and walked Betsey about twenty feet away and back. When the horse was back in place, Mr. Crosby trimmed the hoof. He moved to the rear of the horse and stood beside Betsey's left leg, facing to the rear. Patting her rump, he softly talked to the horse. Checking to see if she would kick him, he touched the back of her leg with his leg. Betsey looked around nervously, but stood still.

The blacksmith hunched over behind the horse with her hind leg between his knees. He kept talking to her as he removed her old shoe and trimmed the hoof.

Next, he moved to the right rear leg. Then to the right foreleg. When all the shoes were off, Mr. Crosby called to Noah. "Come here, boy, and walk her again."

Noah carefully walked Betsey back and forth while the blacksmith checked her gait.

After measuring the hooves to see how large the shoes should be, the smith went to the forge with his hammer in hand. Noah followed. Mr. Crosby put four pieces of iron into the hot coals. With his tools in place, he grabbed a handful of nails from a wooden keg and put them into the pocket of his leather apron.

The iron turned yellow. Grasping one of the iron bars with wooden-handled tongs, the blacksmith brought it to the anvil. Shaping it with his hammer, he bent it over the curved surface of the anvil. Noah's curious mind couldn't wait any longer. He had to ask a question. "What makes the iron melt?" he asked.

"The fire is so hot that it softens the iron enough for me to bend it," the blacksmith explained. "I use my hammer to pound it into the shape that I want." When he had a horseshoe shape, Mr. Crosby called Pa. "Bring your mare over here."

Checking the shape of her trimmed hoof, he measured the hot shoe on the hoof to be sure it was the right size. Pa led the horse away. Mr.

Crosby finished the shoe by laying it on the anvil's wide, flat end. He pounded it. Placing it in the forge, he waited until it was yellow again. Noah moved closer. Sparks flew up from the forge.

The smith used a hole punch and hammer to make holes for the nails. After rounding off the rough ends, he plunged the horseshoe in cold water. It sizzled.

"Why did you do that?" Noah asked.

"To temper it," the blacksmith replied.

"What does *temper* mean?"

"It means to toughen or harden the metal," Mr. Crosby said.

When all four shoes were finished, Pa brought Betsey into position again. The smith placed nails from his apron pocket between his lips. Setting each nail into a hole, he pounded it into the hoof. Noah looked at the man. "Doesn't that hurt Betsey?" he asked.

"No," Mr. Crosby said. "I'm very careful to put the nail in the hoof where the horse won't feel it." Noah was relieved.

When the job was finished, Noah led Betsey while Pa and Mr. Crosby watched to see if she walked properly.

"How long will these shoes last?" he asked when he came back.

"She'll need a trim in about three months," the smith said. "But we may be able to use the same shoes again." Shaking Noah's hand, he said, "You did a fine job helping, young man. Come again."

Pa paid the blacksmith and lifted his young son onto Betsey. As they rode home, Noah talked to Pa about everything he had learned that day.

"Would you like to be a blacksmith when you grow up?" Pa asked.

Noah thought a minute before he answered. *It might be fun to shoe horses and make iron tools.* A look of decision came over his face. "No," he said. "I want to be a schoolmaster."

Pa turned to look at Noah. "Why do you want to be a teacher?"

"Cause then I could have books to read every day," said Noah.

2
The School Boy

September 1764

"Tomorrow you go to school, Noah." Mother Webster made the big announcement in early September.

"Oh, Ma, I'm going to learn to read." Noah's eyes sparkled. "I want to learn all about the stars, and bees, and animals, and flowers." He spread his arms wide. "And everything."

"It may take awhile for that, little one. But someday, God willing, you will know many things." Ma paused. "I pray that above all else, you will put God first. He is the source of all wisdom." She gave him a hug. "Come now. Pa is ready to read the Word of God. After prayer you must go right to bed."

That night, Noah could hardly sleep. A hard rain pounded on the roof. Flashes of lightning made the room bright as daylight. Thunder shook the house. When he finally slept, Noah dreamed about books. Words marched across the pages. He tried to catch them, but they ran away from him. Alphabet letters jumped over each other while Noah watched.

"Cock-a-doodle-do. Get up and go to school," the roosters crowed. Noah awoke. He jumped out of bed and looked out the open window. A cool breeze brushed his face. "I'm coming," he shouted to the roosters.

Running across the bare floor, Noah stopped at the washstand and grabbed a wash cloth. Swish. Into the tin basin and over his face went the cloth. Seeing that Abram had already used the water, Noah dumped it into a bucket and poured fresh water from the pewter pitcher. He swirled the cloth in the basin, squeezed it, and rubbed his face again.

"I feel sorry for Abram," Noah said aloud. "He has to milk cows and work in the fields while I get to read and write."

The older boys could only attend school during the winter. Farm work kept them home during the warmer months.

Sticking his finger into the salt box, Noah quickly rubbed some salt over his teeth. "I wish there was some other way to clean my teeth," he muttered. "I don't like the taste in my mouth." But not even salt in his mouth could spoil Noah's joy this morning. "I'm going to learn to read," he sang. "I'm going to school today."

Pulling the quilt up, Noah quickly made the bed. Fastening his shirt and breeches, he hurried downstairs to eat breakfast with Mercy and Jerusha. Mercy was engaged to be married soon to John Belding. She wouldn't be going to school. Charles was still asleep in the trundle bed beside Ma and Pa's bed in the parlor.

Noah pulled a chair out and sat down. The smell of fried ham filled the air. Steaming corn bread, hot out of the brick oven in the chimney, made Noah's mouth water. *I wish Ma would sit down and pray so we could eat.*

"Thank you, Lord, for the night's rest, and for the bountiful crops," Mother prayed. "Be with the men as they work in the fields." She prayed for each child, by name, and asked for divine protection for them during the day. "Bless Noah as he begins school today. Help him to learn much and to obey the schoolmaster."

Noah fidgeted. *Why does she have to pray so long today? I don't want to be late my first day of school.*

As soon as Ma finished praying, Noah buttered his corn bread. Stuffing it into his mouth, he brushed the remaining crumbs off his lap. "It's good, Ma. Please excuse me." Noah got up and started to leave the table.

"Get back here, young man. You haven't eaten any ham or had anything to drink."

Noah swallowed a piece of ham and gulped some apple cider from the pewter mug. Picking up the shiny tin pail that Mother had filled for his lunch, he started for the door.

"Whoa there, son. Wait for your sister," Mother exclaimed. Noah came back, gave his mother a hug, then rushed out the kitchen door. Down the dirt road he went, ahead of Jerusha. Usually he noticed every flower and weed along the way. But not today.

"Hurry up. I don't want to be late," he called, as his sister followed him along the path. It was a bright, sunny day, but water from last night's rain stood in the ruts. Noah ran and jumped over a puddle. His bare feet squished in the mud when he landed on the other side.

"Slow down, little brother," Jerusha said. "Are you planning to run all the way to school?"

"Yes," Noah shouted.

"You can't go inside anyway until the teacher rings the bell." Jerusha shook her head. No use.

She might as well be talking to the wind. Her brother was almost out of sight.

Noah ran and jumped. Pretending to be a horse, he galloped down the road. A rabbit hopped out of the weeds as Noah dashed past.

"I'm gonna learn to read," he yelled to the startled bunny.

Nearing the schoolhouse, Noah looked at it with increasing excitement. He didn't notice the leaky roof or unpainted boards. It didn't matter that the floor was dirt and that there were no maps or comfortable desks inside. It was his dream come true.

Noah remembered sitting during long sermons at the meetinghouse, thinking about the one-room school building next door. He didn't have to imagine what school was like anymore. He was actually there.

Jerusha arrived just as the teacher came out to pull the bell rope. Waiting in line with the other children, Noah thought his heart would burst through his shirt. It was pounding so hard. Jerusha came and stood beside him.

The schoolmaster, standing on the doorstep, faced the children. "Please line up by ages," he said.

"I'll help you find a seat when we get inside," Jerusha whispered in Noah's ear, as she went farther back in the line. Her kind eyes looked into his. "I remember what it was like two years ago when I started to school."

Noah marched in with the other children who were five years old. When he was inside the building, he waited for his sister.

Taking his hand, Jerusha led him to a seat right in front of the schoolmaster. Noah sat down and looked forward. A birch rod lay on top of the teacher's desk, beside the ink bottle. Noah thought about the time when the teacher had whacked Abram with a stick when he didn't know the answer to a question. Noah sat quietly in his seat, almost afraid to move. He looked around the room.

Older children sat at desks too small for them. Their legs stuck out to the side because they couldn't get them under the table. The table tops were scratched with deep grooves where initials had been carved. Wood was piled beside the fireplace, ready for cold days.

Noah looked at his teacher. He was tall with stringy black hair. His black eyes seemed to look right through you.

"Everyone stand for prayer," the schoolmaster announced. Noah stood up and bowed his head while the teacher prayed a long prayer. After he finished, the schoolmaster told the pupils to be seated while he read the Bible to them. When the long Scripture reading ended, he held up a book: *The New England Primer.*

There were few books in the school; among them the primer, the Holy Bible, and a speller. Showing them the primer, the teacher read a question from it. "Who was the first man?"

Noah raised his hand. "I know, sir," he said. Some of the children snickered as the schoolmaster looked down his long nose at the little boy seated in front of his desk.

"And what is your name, young man? Please stand when you answer a question."

Noah stood beside his desk. "I'm Noah Webster, Junior, and the first man was Adam." He was shaking inside, but proud that he knew the answer.

Noah looked around, searching for Jerusha. She smiled at him and nodded her head. He felt better, knowing that she was there in the room with him.

I wish we'd have our reading class, Noah thought. Finally the time came. Like a swarm of bees, he and the rest of the beginners repeated letter sounds aloud and together.

Ba-be-bi-bo-bu

Ca-ce-ci-so-su

Da-de-di-do-du

I wonder when we'll start to read words? I thought I'd learn to read today. Noah was disappointed.

The schoolmaster asked the older pupils to each pick a younger child to help with ciphering. Jerusha came over to Noah. She showed him how to add numbers together to make a larger number.

When the teacher sent the children out to play after they ate their lunch, Noah joined a group playing tag. A brown-haired girl named Sarah tagged him.

"You're it, Noah," she called, as she ran away from him. Noah chased the little girl but couldn't catch her.

Running inside the schoolhouse, Sarah yelled back, "Can't catch me." Her bright eyes twinkled as she ran to her desk.

When the bell rang, Noah tried to get Sarah's attention, but she was busy practicing writing and wouldn't look at him.

The afternoon went quickly. When the school day ended, Noah walked home with his sister. Kicking stones, he trudged along the narrow path. Dirt, dried by the warm September sun, swirled around his feet. Jerusha skipped along beside him.

"Well, Noah, how was your first day of school?" Mother asked, as the children burst through the doorway.

Noah headed for the water pail and filled a dipper with water. "I'm thirsty," he said. After taking a long drink, he answered. "My desk is right in front of the schoolmaster." With a deep sigh, he looked at his mother. "I thought I'd learn to read today, but I didn't. All we did was make sounds."

Mother patted him on the head. "Just wait a few days," she said. "You'll be reading everything in sight."

Noah walked over to the almanack. Turning the pages, he asked, "Why do some words have big letters and some little?" He pointed to the letter *S* in September.

Mother looked over his shoulder. "The names of things start with big letters. You also put them at the beginning of sentences." She shook her head as she looked at him. "You are such a curious little boy. I wouldn't be surprised if someday you wrote a book yourself."

Noah soon put letters together and made words. Words grew into sentences. He was reading. A little rhyme stood beside each letter in his primer:

A: In *Adam's* fall
We sinned all

all the way to **Z**: *Zaccheus* he
Did climb a tree
His Lord to see.

Noah read the verses over and over. Before long, he had the alphabet memorized, as well as all the verses to go along with it.

One day, Noah carefully copied a prayer from the primer. "Now I lay me down to sleep," he wrote. "I pray Thee, Lord, my soul to keep. If I should die before I wake, I pray Thee, Lord, my soul to take."

The leaking goosequill pen made ink spots all over his paper and his hands. The ink, made from boiled walnut hulls, looked like dark brown freckles. Noah tried to rub the spots off, but they only smeared all over the page.

Noah carried the speckled paper home to show his mother, wondering what she would think.

After Noah read it to her, Ma said, "What a beautiful prayer, son, and you read it so well. I'm proud of you." She didn't mention the spots on the paper. Patting him on the head, she placed the paper on the cupboard beside her writing materials.

The Websters owned several books, but the one they loved best was the Bible. They kept it on a special shelf in the parlor.

"Ma, can I get the Bible and practice reading?" Noah asked after supper. "I washed the ink off my hands, so I won't get it dirty."

Mrs. Webster smiled as she took the big book off the shelf and handed it to the eager boy.

Noah carefully opened the Bible. Sitting quietly, he stared at the words for a long time. *I like the story of Noah taking the animals into the ark before the flood.* Pretending to read the story, he said the words aloud. He knew it by heart. *I wonder if I'm named after Noah in the Bible? Of course, it's Pa's name too. But I think I was named after Noah in the Old Testament.*

Noah often thought about names and their meanings. One day, Pa told him that the name *Webster* meant *a female weaver. That's odd,* Noah thought. *Pa is a weaver all right, and he's a farmer too. But he's not a female.*

"Someday," he said to himself, "I'll read books that tell about the names of everything."

That night Noah stood looking out the window at the stars which glittered so brightly in the frosty autumn air. He always liked to watch them, to think about their size and distance. *How far away are they? What makes them twinkle? I wish I could read something about them.*

As the years went by, Noah read the weekly newspaper, copies of old sermons, schoolbooks, and, of course, the Bible.

Often he went to the garret to read the old almanacks which were stored under the eaves.

There among the cobwebs, old spinning wheels, and dried herbs, Noah discovered a new world of information.

Studying the almanacks, he learned about the planets and the stars. He found out how to raise flax. He read information about everything from the cure for smallpox to the harm of using tobacco and strong drink. All these facts stuck like cockleburs in his mind.

3
The Meetinghouse

January 1769

Shadows danced on the walls as ten-year-old Noah, carrying a flickering candle, climbed the steep stairs to the darkness above. His brothers followed close behind. Opening the door to the south chamber, Noah started inside. Abram and Charles pushed past him into the room, bumping Noah as they went by.

"Watch out," Noah shouted. He carefully placed the homemade white candle on a storage barrel. "Do you want to set the house on fire?"

"Boys, what's going on?" Mother called as she came up the stairs and into the room carrying the warming pan by its long wooden handle.

"Noah's fussing 'cause we bumped into his candle," Abram said. "He wants to read all night."

"Well, they almost knocked it out of my hand," Noah said, looking at his older brother.

The wind swished around the corner of the house and rattled the windows. Mother shook her head. "It's a mighty cold night. Stop your quarreling and get ready for bed." She pulled the quilt back. "In just a minute, I'll have your covers as hot as bread right out of the oven."

Her three sons watched as she slid the round metal pan filled with hot coals back and forth between the linen sheets.

"All three of you get into bed right away," Mother called, as she went across the hall to Jerusha's room.

Abram and Charles climbed into the bed which the three brothers shared. The featherbed caved in to fit their bodies. Pulling the blue bed quilt up under their chins, the two boys looked at Noah.

"Blow out the candle," Abram ordered his younger brother.

"Not yet," Noah said. "I'm gonna read awhile." When his brothers turned over, Noah lifted the trunk lid and took out a book. His supply of candles was hidden beneath a blanket. Looking at his brothers in their snug nest, Noah almost decided to crawl into bed with them. *Br-r-r, it's cold.* He saw the skim of ice forming in the basin on the dresser. Noah heard his mother go downstairs. The warming pan clanged against the brick as she set it beside the kitchen fireplace. Placing his hands on either side of the flickering candle, Noah steadied the flame in the drafty room.

Sitting on a low stool, he looked at the title of the book. "Pilgrim's Progress," he whispered. "By John Bunyan. And only two chapters left to read. I can't wait to finish it." Shading the light with one hand, he shivered as the room grew colder. When the candle finally burned down to a pool of wax, the chilled boy closed the book and crawled into bed with his sleeping brothers. In spite of the howling wind, Noah fell asleep.

"Boys. Wake up. It's time to get ready to go to church," Pa called up the stairs. Noah opened his eyes. It couldn't be morning already. He looked across the room. A sprinkling of snow dusted the floor under the window. Solid ice covered the basin. He burrowed deeper into the featherbed.

"Boys! I don't hear you getting up," Father yelled. Abram and Charles climbed out of bed and gave Noah a shove.

"Get up, you lazy redhead. You shouldn't have read so late last night," six-year-old Charles teased.

Smoothing down his bushy hair, Noah rolled over and closed his eyes, trying to ignore his brothers.

Yanking the quilt off the bed, Abram warned, "Pa's going to be coming up the stairs any minute. You better get up."

With a groan, Noah slid over the edge of the bed and put his feet on the cold, bare floor. "Yowee! It feels like ice," he cried. His toes curled up as he hopped over the icy boards.

Pulling on their homemade breeches, woolen stockings, and leather shoes, the boys wasted no time in getting dressed.

Noah took his linen shirt from a wooden peg on the wall. "I watched Ma press this with the sad iron yesterday. I wonder why they're called *sad* irons? Is it because Ma is sad when she irons?"

"No," Abram said, "It's because they're so heavy."

"Why are they so heavy?" Noah asked.

"I suppose because they're made of iron," Abram said. "You ask too many questions."

Although Noah still didn't understand the sad part, he stored the information away in his active mind.

"Something smells good down below," he said, sniffing the air. "Ma must be frying ham."

"Well, if you don't hurry up you won't get any breakfast," Abram warned.

Breaking the ice off the top of the basin, the three brothers hurriedly washed their faces and hands in the freezing water. They raced downstairs. Jerusha already sat at the long table with Pa. Noah slid onto the wooden bench while Mistress Webster poured mugs of hot cider for everyone. Bowing his head, Pa said, "Let us pray." Each one of the family members sat with heads bowed as Pa thanked God for the food.

After Mr. Webster finished his lengthy prayer, his wife brought huge platters of johnnycakes and ham to the table.

"Pass the maple syrup, please," Noah said. "I smelled the ham frying, Ma. It sure looks good."

"Noah stayed up half the night reading," Abram reported.

"Is that right, son?" Mr. Webster said, looking sternly at Noah. "You know that our Sabbath begins at sundown Saturday. No more reading on the Sabbath for you, young man."

"I'm sorry, Pa. I was so interested in the book that I couldn't stop. I have to give it back to the pastor today. He lent it to me last week."

"What book is it?" Ma asked.

"It's called *Pilgrim's Progress.* It's about finding the way to heaven. I'm sorry I read on the Sabbath."

He paused. How could he explain his feelings? No one understood how he felt about reading and learning things. "I wish we owned more books," he said.

"We farmers can't afford to order books from Great Britain," Pa explained. "And there are none printed here in New England."

Pa knew that Noah was different from his brothers and sisters. Noah soaked up knowledge like a newly plowed field soaks up rain. He wanted to read and learn everything he could. Pa felt sorry for his son, but there was nothing that he could do about it.

"Eat your johnnycake, boy, before it gets cold. We can't do anything about books right now. They're too expensive," Pa continued with a frown. "We have to pay extra money for the things we buy from England. They're taxing us to death."

Noah lowered his head. He bit his lip hard. Shielding his eyes with his hands, he felt the hot tears starting to run down his cheeks. It was useless to ask for something he couldn't have, but he wanted books more than anything else in the world.

While Ma and Jerusha cleared the table, Pa and the boys put on coats and mufflers and went out into a white world. "We'll have to take the cutter today," Mr. Webster announced.

Pa had made the cutter out of long wooden boards, curved on the side. The blacksmith put metal runners on it. There was a high back seat where the driver and his passengers sat. The children usually sat under robes on the floor of the cutter. With a large family it was crowded, but snug and warm for those sitting below.

Pa backed old Betsey into the shafts of the cutter. The two long, narrow pieces of wood curved around the horse's body and were fastened to the collar by leather straps. Bells, mounted on the straps, jingled merrily in the frosty air.

"Can I hold the reins, Pa?" Noah asked.

"All right, but first come and help me load the foot stoves. Get the robes, too."

Noah carried a foot stove in each hand. The small, square, metal boxes had holes punched in the sides to let out the heat. Filled with hot coals from the fireplace, they made a warm footstool.

Abram brought the robes. With the fur side next to their bodies, the Websters kept warm in spite of the weather.

"The meetinghouse will really be cold today." Father's breath came out in frosty puffs of air. "Must be down to zero this morning. We better take Rhoda along." Dogs were allowed inside the meetinghouse. Lying on their masters' feet, they provided much-needed warmth. If they barked or disturbed anyone, they were taken outside.

Mr. Webster whistled, and the dog leaped in the cutter. "Noah, go tell your Ma to come," Pa said.

When everyone was seated, Noah slapped the reins on the mare's back. She broke into a trot as they headed down the ridge. The horse knew the way well enough. The Websters never missed a church service, even when it was below zero.

Noah reached down and warmed his cold fingers in Rhoda's fur. She licked his hand with her rough tongue. Her wet nose nuzzled against his knee. "I'm glad we brought you along," Noah said. The warmth of Rhoda's body warmed his legs as the metal runners flew along the snow-packed road.

Holding tightly to the reins as they went down the road, Noah noticed other families getting their cutters and larger sleighs ready. Above each house the smoke rose straight up from the chimneys.

Fourth Church, in the west division of Hartford, was less than a mile from the Webster home, but on a day like this it would be difficult to walk through the drifts. *Pa and*

Abram and I could make it, Noah thought. *Ma and Jerusha with their long skirts couldn't.*

As they came near the meetinghouse, Noah saw the minister walking across the road toward the church. His black suit stood out like a stove pipe against the white snow. Noah cracked the whip and drove smartly into the churchyard.

"Whoa, girl. Here we are." He eased the cutter up to the horse block so Ma and Jerusha could get out. Pa jumped out to help them step down. After unhitching the mare and tying her to a hitching post, Noah joined the rest of the family as they walked toward the meetinghouse.

The church, a plain clapboard building, had a narrow path leading to the front door. Windows along the sides of the building let in both light and cold air.

With Rhoda at his heels, Noah stopped to read the notices posted on the door. Along with a list of town officers, he saw a notice of a cattle sale to be held next week. There was also a marriage announcement. "Anyone objecting to this union must post his reasons on this door," Noah read aloud.

"Look at this, Ma. I wonder if there'll be any objections here when we come next Sunday?"

"Come along, Noah," Mother urged. "You can't stand there reading all morning. We must go inside."

Since Pa was a deacon of the church, the Webster pew was near the front of the sanctuary. Noah and Rhoda filed in behind the family, and Noah sat down on the high-backed bench. His family had owned this pew for as long as he could remember.

Looking up, Noah saw the minister walk to the platform and stand behind the square pulpit. Rhoda settled down on the floor. Noah liked to have her lie on his feet to keep them warm. There was no heat in the building. Most of the women and children had brought foot stoves. Noah could smell the burning charcoal as Pa placed their stoves on the floor. He felt some heat coming out the little holes in the sides of the stoves. They were warm at first, but if the sermon was too long, the hot coals burned out.

After the congregation sang a psalm, the minister stood at the pulpit to pray. Noah fidgeted while the pastor prayed on and on.

Sundays seemed endless to Noah. Besides the long prayer, the pastor's sermons lasted for hours. Today it was freezing cold inside. Noah looked up at the minister. The pulpit was so high that he had to tip his head back to see the pastor's black suit coat and powdered wig. Behind the minister were two shelves holding lighted candles.

Noah liked to watch the spectacles bounce up and down on the preacher's nose as he talked. When the pastor spoke, little puffs of white floated into the frosty air. To Noah, they looked like periods at the ends of sentences. He reached down and petted Rhoda on her head. *At least my feet are warm, even though my fingers are numb.* As the preacher droned on, Noah's mind wandered.

Moving closer to Pa, he let his thoughts drift back to last summer. The Websters often brought a picnic dinner with them. Joining other families on the shady side of the meeting-house, they ate their cold chicken and blue-berry pie. Ma's biscuits were washed down with cold cider. Noah recalled how good it tasted on a hot July afternoon.

After the picnic meal, one of the deacons often read a sermon to the boys and girls. Chil-dren were never permitted to play on the Lord's

Day. No jumping or running was allowed, so they sat in the shade and talked after the sermon. If anyone fished, hunted, sailed, rowed, or did any work on the farm from sunset Saturday to sunset Sunday, he was punished by a fine or a whipping.

I wonder how long this sermon will be, Noah thought. *Rhoda's getting restless.*

Noah's mind wandered again. He thought about their Sundays at home. After church, when dinner was over, the Webster children would sit on chairs in the parlor. While Abram played the flute, they would sing psalms. Noah liked to sing. His clear voice usually stood out above the others.

The minister was getting near the end of his sermon. Noah could tell because Rhoda was moving around at his feet. It was funny how she always seemed to know when the preacher was nearly finished. Glancing over at Charles, Noah saw that he was sleeping against Ma.

Looking out the window, he noticed icy pellets of snow spitting against the glass. From where he sat, Noah could see the schoolhouse. *I wonder if the schoolmaster is in church today.* Noah turned his head. The back of the pew was so high that he couldn't see anyone behind him.

Mother looked at Noah and nodded her head toward the preacher. Noah knew what that meant. *Stop gawking and pay attention.*

I'll probably hear from her later, he thought. He stared at the pulpit.

Just yesterday Pa had mentioned that they should take some firewood to the parsonage. Their pastor, Rev. Nathaniel Hooker, didn't get paid for preaching. He earned money tutoring boys who planned to go to college. People brought meat and vegetables to put food on his table, and they gave him wood to heat his house. Noah knew that the minister had at least twenty books in his library. *I'd rather have books than money,* Noah thought. *Someday I'd like to have a library of my own.* Suddenly he remembered the book he had borrowed. *I'll get it from the cutter after church. I hope it isn't covered with snow,* he worried.

Noah started thinking about his future. *I'd like to go to college to learn to be a schoolmaster. Or maybe a lawyer. I don't think I want to be a minister.*

The wind began to whine. *It sounds like a blizzard coming.* Noah turned his head to look out the window. White snow lined each pane. Only a peephole was clear now. Rhoda raised her head and gave a low growl. Fortunately, the pastor was asking everyone to rise for the closing prayer. Standing with the others, Noah bowed his head.

After the prayer, he grabbed Rhoda and led her back down the aisle. Several of his friends spoke to him as he went by.

"Do you think we'll get snowbound?" John Mix asked.

"It looks like it," Noah said.

"If we don't have school tomorrow, let's go sledding," said John's brother Samuel.

"I'm gonna see the pastor about some books," Noah replied.

"Oh, you always have your nose in a book," Samuel grumbled as Noah went past.

Walking toward the door, Noah noticed Sarah sitting with her parents. A shy smile crossed her face as she saw him glancing her way. Brown hair covering her face, she ducked her head. Ever since the first day of school, when she tagged him, Noah had noticed the pretty, dark-eyed Sarah. He walked on down the aisle. Noah spoke to the pastor at the church door.

"I finished reading your book," he said.

"What did you think of it?"

"Some of the words were hard, but I sounded them out. I figured what they meant by the way they were used in sentences," Noah said.

"What did you like best about the story?" the minister asked.

"I liked the part where Pilgrim and Hopeful escape from the dungeon of Giant Despair."

"It's a wonderful allegory, isn't it?"

"What's an allegory?" Noah asked. "I like to learn new words like that."

"An allegory is a story using symbolic figures and actions to teach a truth."

Noah looked puzzled. The minister explained, "It's a story with a hidden spiritual meaning."

"Oh, I understand," Noah said. "There really wasn't a Giant Despair. He was just a symbol of the way we sometimes feel."

"Exactly," the pastor replied. "You really did get the hidden meaning."

Noah felt someone nudge his arm. It was Pa. "Come on, son. Other people want to talk to the pastor."

"That's all right," the minister said. "You have a fine boy. We were just discussing the book he borrowed." He shook Pa's hand, and the Webster family went out the door.

Ducking his head, Noah walked into the biting wind. Running to the cutter, he remembered the book. He found it under the lap robe. *Good. It's dry. No damage done.* He tucked it under his coat and ran back to the church.

"Here's your book and thank you very much," Noah gasped.

"You're welcome. Perhaps we can find another one that you would enjoy. John Bunyan wrote another story called *The Holy War.*"

"I'd like to read that," Noah said. "I must go now. Thank you again."

The harsh wind and bitter cold didn't stop the song in Noah's heart as he thought about getting another book to read.

Outside, Pa was helping Ma and Jerusha into the cutter. With long skirts flapping and bonnet strings blowing, they climbed over the edge. When they were settled inside, Pa took the reins. Plowing through three-foot drifts, the horse did her best to pull the cutter toward home. Mistress Webster and Jerusha huddled under the robes, but the boys and Rhoda sat up beside Pa. Noah enjoyed riding in the snow, even though sharp bits of ice stung his cheeks. With bells jingling, they bounced along the road.

"Did you return the book, Noah?" asked Pa.

"Yes, I did. And pastor said I could borrow another one. I told him you were bringing them some firewood. May we go tomorrow, please?"

Pa smiled. "I never saw the likes of you," he said, "but we'll see. Perhaps you boys can help me load the wood on the stone boat and we'll take it over."

Noah grinned back. "It would help pack the road too, wouldn't it?"

"Certainly should," said Pa. "We've carried a good many boulders on it, and you can always see the trail it leaves behind in the fields."

"Maybe I can look at the minister's books when we take the firewood tomorrow," Noah said.

Pa looked at Noah. "I believe you'd rather read than do anything else."

"That's right," Noah agreed. "I love books and I love words. When I'm older I want to talk to the pastor about learning to read Latin. Most of his books are written in Latin."

Pa shook his head and flicked the reins over the mare's back. When they arrived home, Noah jumped out and helped Ma and the girls out of the cutter.

On his way to the barn, Noah thought about the next day when he could see the pastor's library. Even though he dreamed about going to college, Noah didn't dare mention it to Pa yet. *Maybe I can talk to the minister about it some other time*, he thought.

But he never had a chance to do this. When Noah was twelve, his pastor, Nathaniel Hooker, died.

4
The Farm Boy

May 1772

Sunlight lay like a soft yellow rug on the lawn. Tree leaves, wearing their new green coats, rustled softly in the early morning breeze.

Thirteen-year-old Noah stopped to smell the fragrant lilac blossoms on the bush beside the front door. Standing on the flat doorstep in front of his house, he looked around the yard. Spring was here. Two plump robins cocked their heads as they hopped in the wet grass. Suddenly, one of them yanked a long worm from the damp ground.

Noah watched with interest. *Who taught birds to eat earthworms? How do they digest them?* So many questions went through his mind. *I want to learn all I can about every-thing.*

Looking eastward toward the town of Hartford, he saw the Connecticut River glimmering like a shiny thread in the distance. *What was beyond the river?*

"What are you dreaming about, boy?" Pa interrupted, coming out of the house.

Noah looked up. "I was just thinking that I'd like to travel and learn how people live in the other colonies. Maybe I'll even go to England or France someday."

"You wouldn't be very happy in England right now," Pa said. He looked at his son. "You haven't forgotten the Boston Massacre, have you?"

"No. I wonder what's happening in Massachusetts now," Noah said. "It's been two years since the massacre. Do you suppose the British redcoats will come this far south? Will there be war?"

"There probably will be war before too long," Pa said. "But right now we've got chores to do. The cows need to be milked. When that's done, I want you to head out to the back pasture and get some stones hauled out. The stone boat is already out there. Load it up and I'll get the ox ready and bring her out."

"All right, Pa," Noah said. Whistling to Rhoda, he headed for the pasture.

Noah worked hard on his father's ninety-acre farm in West Hartford. Besides helping clear stony fields, he drove a team of horses and walked behind a plow. With his dog, he kept the cattle from straying.

In summer there was corn to hoe, berries to pick, hay to cut, and potatoes to dig. Butchering, in the fall, meant carrying hot water, sharpening tools, and preparing sausage skins. Sometimes Noah's friends, John and Samuel Mix, came to visit and stayed to help.

In winter he carried wood inside and shoveled paths to the outbuildings. And all year he milked cows. Morning and evening.

Arriving in the field, Noah walked past stone fences bordering the pasture. He began to lift heavy rocks onto the stone boat.

When Pa came out with the ox, Noah asked about the stone fences. "Who made all these fences, Pa?"

"Our ancestors did. When they arrived, they cleared the land for farming. They removed trees, brush, and stones so the fields could be planted."

"Tell me about our ancestors," Noah said.

"Well, your great-great-great-grandfather, John Webster, came to the Connecticut River valley years ago with Thomas Hooker's group."

"Was Thomas Hooker related to our minister, Reverend Hooker?"

"I'm sure they were related," Pa said. "But, don't forget, this was about a hundred years ago. Thomas Hooker was a minister too. He and his congregation left their homes and lands in Newtown, Massachusetts, and traveled a hundred miles on foot to Connecticut."

"How many were in their group?"

"There were 110 men, women, and children plus more than a hundred cattle and pigs."

Noah whistled. "It must have taken them a long time to walk here."

"It took two weeks. They sang psalms as they walked through the woods. Sometimes they spent the night outside an Indian village and shared food with the natives. Often they were alone in the wilderness." Pa helped Noah lift an extra large boulder. Sitting on the edge of the stone boat, he continued his story. "At last they arrived on the east bank of our Connecticut River. They wondered how they could take humans and livestock across the rushing current."

"What did they do?" Noah asked.

Pa thought a minute. "I believe it was an Indian chief named Waginacut who came to their aid. He asked all the nearby Indians to bring canoes and rafts to carry the group across the river." Pa stood up, but kept talking. "When they all arrived safely on the west bank, there were prayers of thanksgiving and songs of praise. The town of Hartford was begun."

"My teacher said it was originally named Suckiaug," Noah said.

"That was the Indian name for their village," Pa agreed. "It means black earth. They grew beautiful fields of corn on the rich bottom land."

"Didn't we learn the right time to plant corn from the Indians?" Noah asked.

"Yes, when the leaves of the oak tree are the size of a mouse's ear we plant our corn," Pa said. "The Indians also taught the newcomers how to make succotash with corn and beans."

Noah smacked his lips. "I'm glad we learned how to do that. I like the way Ma fixes it. Did the Indians dry their corn to make cornmeal, like we do?"

"Right," Pa agreed. "They always ground it by hand. Now we have our gristmills with water wheels providing the power."

Noah looked at the sun. It was right above them. "Isn't it time to head to the house for dinner?" he asked. His back ached from lifting rocks. He was hungry too.

"I suppose we can quit for now. We've got the stone boat nearly loaded. As soon as it's pulled out of the pasture, we'll go in and see what Ma has ready for us."

Walking with his father toward the farmhouse while Rhoda trailed behind, Noah looked at the Farmington hills in the southwest. Soft green valleys contrasted with the bright blue sky above. They passed the apple orchard and stopped by the well. The water in the well was always cool and refreshing. Noah liked to drink it. *Nothing tastes better on a hot day*, he decided. He drew some water for Rhoda, then poured some from the bucket into a tin cup and swallowed it in quick gulps.

While Pa unhitched the ox, Noah went to the washstand. After washing his hands in a tin basin on the wooden bench, Noah took the dipper and poured water over his head. The cold water ran down his neck and under his shirt. Slapping the damp material, he felt the cool wetness on his chest. *That feels better.* He wiped his sweaty face on his shirt sleeve and walked to the side door.

The heat of the kitchen hit Noah in the face when he opened the door. *Baked beans today,* he thought. *And freshly baked bread.*

Mother pulled a pie out of the brick oven with the peel (a long-handled shovel). Noah went toward her. "Can I help you, Ma?" Without waiting for an answer, he picked up a cloth and lifted the pie off the shovel. "Why is it called a peel?" he asked. "Where did the name come from?"

"I don't know, son. You are certainly a most unusual child. Always wanting to know what words mean." She paused. "I wonder where you got your curiosity."

"Maybe I got it from my ancestors. Pa told me about my great-great-great-grandfather today, when we were out in the pasture," Noah said. "What about your ancestors, Ma?"

Mistress Webster wiped her sweaty forehead with her apron. "The most famous one in my family was William Bradford, who was governor of the Plymouth Colony for thirty-seven years."

"How was he related to you?"

"He was my great-great-grandfather." She smiled. "He came over on the *Mayflower* and was a man of God. His book is the main record of the Pilgrims."

Noah's eyes lit up. "You mean he wrote a book? What's it called?"

"I believe the name of it is *History of Plymouth Plantation*," she said. "Perhaps we can get a copy of it for you to read some day."

Ma moved quickly toward the table. "I can't spend any more time talking. Here comes your Pa. He'll want to eat right away."

Noah sat down. There were so many things to think about. *My ancestors were really important people. I'd like to read that book about the Pilgrims. I wonder who has a copy of it.*

Charles slid on the bench. "What are you dreaming about?" he asked.

"Nothing," Noah replied. The rest of the family gathered around the table. After they were all seated, Pa prayed.

As soon as he finished, Charles spoke, "Did you hear about our new pastor?"

"No, what's his name?"

"Nathan Perkins. He just moved into the parsonage today."

Noah looked at his father. Being a deacon at the church, Mr. Webster knew almost everything about everybody. "Is that right, Pa? Where's he from?"

"He recently graduated from Princeton," Noah Webster, Senior, replied.

"Are colleges just for teaching ministers?" Charles asked.

Pa finished eating a mouthful of baked beans before he answered. "Most of them started out for that purpose," he said. "The minister was the community leader. Often he taught school and settled disputes. So he was a lawyer and a teacher as well as the pastor. But now our colleges are teaching young men to be doctors and lawyers as well as ministers."

"And schoolmasters," Noah added.

"Yes, some schoolmasters have attended college. I don't believe that yours did, but I've heard of some who have."

"Can we go down to meet Mr. Perkins?" Noah asked.

"No, we should let him get settled first," Pa said. "We better eat our dinner now before these beans get cold."

"I know why Noah wants to meet him," Abram teased.

"Why?" Charles said.

"He wants to check out the minister's books."

Noah's sunburned face turned even

redder. "So what if I do," he snapped. "It's none of your business."

"Boys, settle down," Father said. "Eat your dinner and forget the books. I'm ready for some of Ma's hot apple pie. If only we could have a cup of tea with it."

Mrs. Webster shook her finger at him. "You know we aren't drinking tea, as long as the British tax us for it."

"I know. I'm willing to do without the tea, but I do miss it," Pa said, as he washed his pie down with apple cider.

The next day, Noah begged his father to let him go to meet the new minister.

"When you're done with your chores, you may go," Pa said. "But don't stay long. Rev. Perkins is busy."

Noah milked the cows so fast that they hardly had time to swish their tails in his face. He left the milk bucket with Abram. "Will you finish the milking so I can go now?" he asked.

"What's your big rush, Noah?"

"I want to see if the minister will teach me to read Latin," Noah replied.

"All right. I'll do your work." He gave Noah a playful slap on the back. "I'm sorry I teased you last night."

"Thanks, Abram. I'll help you when I get back."

Noah went to the south chamber and took off his dirty shirt and breeches. He slicked down his hair with water from the basin. With clean clothes and wet hair, he rushed toward the parsonage. It was a small frame house across the road from the church.

Noah ran up to the minister's front door. Smoothing down his hair, he suddenly felt shy and almost decided to turn around and go home. Noah hesitated. He was just starting to knock when the door burst open.

"Come in. Come in. My name is Nathan Perkins. Good to meet you. What may I do for you?"

Stepping inside, Noah said, "I'm Noah Webster, Junior. We live down the road. I wanted to talk to you about tutoring me."

He looked around the room. Four ladder-back chairs and some wooden stools were on one side of the room. A barrel filled with books sat on the floor.

"Do you need help unpacking your books?" he asked.

The new pastor saw the eagerness in the boy's eyes. "Do you like to read?" he said.

"Yes, sir, I do. I want to learn to read Latin too, so I can go to college."

"How old are you, Noah?"

"Fourteen, sir, come next October."

Nathan Perkins smiled. "It would take about two years. I believe we could get you ready for Yale College by the fall of seventy-four. I'll speak to your father about it."

On the way back, Noah felt like he was walking on air. *I'm going to learn to read Latin. I hope Pa will say yes.* The long walk seemed like nothing. Carrying the Latin grammar book that the minister gave him, Noah said aloud, "I'll study it every day and learn it perfectly."

Arriving at the farmhouse, he hurried to his chamber and put the book in the old trunk.

After changing his clothes, he headed for the barn and found Abram.

"I'm back." He picked up a pitchfork and began cleaning up the barn floor.

"You seem mighty happy," Abram said.

"I am. I'm going to learn to read Latin. The pastor said he would tutor me."

The two boys worked together until the work was done. They walked to the well and cleaned up before entering the house.

"Noah, would you get me some flour from the shop?" Ma asked as they came in the door. "I need some for making pies. Here's a pan."

Noah went across the road to the building that Pa and Uncle Daniel used for weaving and storage. Behind the loom stood a big barrel full of flour. *Pa works hard,* Noah thought. *Trying to make a living by farming and weaving keeps him busy.* Filling the pan with flour, Noah carefully shook it to let it settle and carried it into the kitchen.

That night at the supper table, Noah was the center of attention.

"What's the new pastor like?" Ma asked.

"Well, he's young and nice. He's willing to tutor me so I can go to college," Noah blurted out.

"College!" Pa almost shouted. "Where do you think we'll find money for that?"

"Oh, Pa, I want to go so badly. Please let

me study with him. He's gonna talk to you about it."

"I don't know, Noah," Pa said, "it takes about all we have to feed our family. We can't do much more."

"What's a tutor?" Charles interrupted.

"A tutor is someone who teaches privately— a schoolmaster without a school," Noah said.

"Oh," Charles said, "you already know everything. Why do you want to learn more?"

"I don't know everything," Noah said. "Just pass the potatoes, please." He wished he had let the pastor talk to Pa first. Noah didn't say anything more during the meal.

Noah carried the Latin book to the field with him every morning. Whenever there was time to sit and rest, he opened it. Latin was like an exciting puzzle. He studied every page and remembered what he read. Memorizing the rules was the most fun.

One afternoon, Father came by as Noah sat under an apple tree reading the grammar. When a shadow crossed his page, Noah looked up. "Pa, I have to learn Latin," he began, expecting to be scolded.

"I know, son. Just don't neglect your work."

"Has the pastor talked to you yet?" Noah asked.

"Yes. I told him that you could study with him. We'll pay him somehow." He paused with a serious look on his face. "Your Ma and I talked it over and decided to do our best to help you get to college. We may have to do without some things, but we believe you should go to school."

"Oh, thank you, Pa!" Noah looked at his father. "I'll do my best to make you proud of me some day."

"I'm proud of you now, son. It's just that I don't quite know how to get all the bills paid." Sitting down beside Noah, he sighed. "Prices are high. England taxes us on everything we import. We don't have any voice in it so we're at their mercy."

"Do you think we'll ever be free from their rule over us?" Noah asked.

"Probably not, without war," Pa said, "and it looks like we're headed in that direction."

"I wish I could help," Noah said.

"The best help you can do right now is to get back to plowing that field."

"All right, Pa. Thank you for letting me study with Mr. Perkins."

The next day, Noah took the Latin book back to the minister.

"How did it go, Noah?"

"Fine, sir. I learned all the rules in just two weeks. I can turn Latin into English and English into Latin."

The pastor gave him a test. Noah's paper was perfect.

****

Off and on for two years, Noah studied with the minister. Finally, Mr. Perkins gave him a certificate saying that he was ready for college. Mr. Webster saw how determined Noah was to get an education. He watched as his son studied day and night, spending time with his books instead of going to parties or playing games.

One evening, at the supper table, Pa gave Noah some exciting news. "We have enough money saved for you to go to college."

"Oh, Pa," Noah couldn't go on. His voice choked. He was thrilled to hear that his expenses would be paid, but he knew it was a great sacrifice that his parents were making. *I wonder if I can ever pay them back.*

Charles and Abram didn't look too happy about the news. They knew that there wouldn't be much money left over to help them in their future plans.

The night before he was to leave for Yale, Noah joined the family in the kitchen for their usual time of prayer and Bible reading. Bring-

ing the old Bible from the parlor shelf, he sat
with Abram, Charles, and Jerusha in front of
the huge fireplace. The warmth and light of the
fire drew them together. Drying herbs and
vegetables hung from the whitewashed walls.

I'll miss this nightly time with my family,
Noah thought. *The smell of herbs. The big
fireplace. Ma's cooking. I'll miss Sarah too.
Life at Yale will be different. I can't believe I'm
really going to college. But I am!* Joy overcame
his sad thoughts as he realized that his dream
was coming true.

Father Webster, wearing his night cap to
cover his bald head, took the Bible in his big
hands. The glow of the fire reflected on his
serious face.

What beautiful words, Noah thought, as he
heard about God's love. *I know that the Bible is
more than just words to Ma and Pa. They live
by what it teaches. I wonder if someday I can
know God like my parents do?* Noah's mind
was full of questions as he knelt to pray with
his family.

5
The College Boy

September 1774

Noah was so excited that he couldn't sleep. *Tomorrow is the day I leave for college. I'll have books to read. Lessons to learn. Teachers to meet. I wonder if Sarah will miss me?* A jumble of thoughts kept the fifteen-year-old awake until dawn crept into the room. He finally slept.

The next thing he knew, the roosters were crowing. Jumping out of bed, Noah woke Charles. "It's time to get up. This is the day I leave for Yale."

Charles yawned and turned over. "All right. Let me sleep a few more minutes."

I wonder if Charles is looking forward to having only two in the bed after I leave. Noah looked at his younger brother. *Charles is growing up. But it's still hard to get him up in the morning.*

Abram must be already out in the barn doing chores. Cows have to be milked even on special days like today. When Abram gets married to Rachel Merrill, Charles will have the room to himself. Noah shook his head. *But he'll also have Abram's and my chores to do.*

The morning was crisp. Noah knew that it would soon be warm because sunshine was pouring into the room. He packed his clothing and two quilts with the few books that he owned and took them downstairs.

Ma gave him some sheets and candles to add to his bundle. Along with his new suit and overcoat, which were already in the saddlebags on Father's horse, Noah added a jug of cider and some corn bread to eat along the way. He and his father prepared to walk the thirty-five miles to Yale College.

At the door of the farmhouse, Mrs. Webster stood, waving goodbye. Jerusha, Abram, and Charles stood beside her.

"God keep you, son," Noah's mother called as she watched him walk down the dirt path. She rubbed her eyes with a handkerchief. "Be good, and do your best."

Noah looked back. It was hard to say goodbye to Ma. Seeing the tears run down her cheeks made him want to cry. His throat felt like a lump of bread was stuck in it. "I'll do my best to make you proud of me. Goodbye." He waved to her as long as he could see her standing beside the door.

Noah and his father traveled all day. They took turns riding the horse. Arriving in New Haven just as the sun was setting, they tied the mare to a hitching post and walked on the campus.

"Welcome to Brick Prison," a boy yelled as they walked past him. *I wonder why he called it a prison,* Noah thought. *It's a dream come true for me.* Later, Noah learned why it was called a prison. He found out that the students could go only where they were told. Sometimes he too felt like a prisoner when he was closely watched.

Mr. Webster and Noah saw three buildings. Entering the nearest one, they asked for the president of the college. Dr. Napthali Daggett came slowly out of his office and introduced himself. A heavyset man, he wore a black robe, white wig, and a high cocked hat.

"Would you like a tour of our campus?" he asked.

"Yes, sir, we'd appreciate that," Noah said. He looked at the president. *I wonder if Dr. Daggett will take us himself. His overstuffed body doesn't seem to move very fast.*

"Let me get your class tutor to show you around," the president said. "His name is Joseph Buckminster. There are forty freshmen under his supervision."

When Mr. Buckminster arrived, Noah noticed that he, too, wore a robe and that he didn't look much older than the students. Noah and his father followed the tutor into a brick building.

"This is our chapel," Mr. Buckminster explained. "We meet here every morning for prayers." Noah saw rows of benches facing a platform on which a high pulpit stood.

Going into another part of the building, they saw the library. Noah looked at the books. They were old and dusty and evidently not used much. But Noah's eyes lit up. *Oh, so many books. I wonder how many there are?* Mr. Buckminster saw him looking at the shelves. "We have 2,500 volumes in our library," he said. "Unfortunately, freshmen are not allowed to take books out of the library."

Noah frowned. He tried to keep his disappointment from showing as they went on.

"Here is the museum," their guide said, as he led them into a cluttered room. Moth-eaten stuffed birds and animals rested on counter tops. A few dusty fossils and a variety of stones sat on open shelves. Noah read the labels beneath each display. The dust made him sneeze, but he was interested in all the new information.

Outside, taking deep breaths of fresh air, they walked to the next building. Noah noticed that the upperclassmen wore robes. *The students in plain clothes, like mine, must be freshmen. I'm glad I don't have to wear a robe or hat this year.*

"This is your dormitory," Mr. Buckminster said, as they came near an old brick building. "It's called Connecticut Hall. You may bring your things in later." He pointed toward the back. "The pump and privy are out there. Also the wood. You boys will have to split it for the fireplaces."

They walked on toward a rickety wooden building painted blue. "We call this Old College Hall," Mr. Buckminster said. "It's the dining hall, another dormitory, recitation hall, and buttery."

"What's in the buttery?" Noah asked.

"You can buy bread and butter, cider and

coffee, and other drinks there," the tutor replied.

When the tour ended, Mr. Webster helped carry the saddle bags into Noah's room. Together, they took out Noah's clothing and books. They found the candles and a tin basin that Ma had put in with the wash cloths, sheets, and quilts.

"I'd better be on my way now. It will soon be dark and I'll have to ride most of the night." Pa put his arm around Noah's shoulder. "Do your best, son."

Noah bit his lip and cleared his throat. "I'll miss you, Pa." He struggled to keep from crying. "Thank you for all you've done for me."

After his father left, Noah put his few belongings away. It seemed strange to be on his own and not have any of his family nearby. His roommate hadn't arrived yet. Noah looked around the room. Four bare walls. Rough wooden floor. A stand with a water pitcher. Two beds.

Taking out the remaining piece of corn bread, Noah ate it slowly to make it last longer. He thought about home. *Ma probably fixed biscuits and gravy and fried chicken for Abram, Charles, and Jerusha tonight. She'll save some biscuits for Pa's breakfast when he gets home.* Thinking about his father finally brought the tears. "I'll never forget how Pa and Ma did without things to get enough money to pay for my schooling at Yale," he said aloud.

Lying down on the straw-filled bed, Noah determined that he would study hard. *I'll do everything I possibly can to repay my parents for their sacrifice.* He was sound asleep when he heard footsteps in the room. *Must be my roommate.*

"Are you awake?" a voice whispered.

"I am now. My name's Noah Webster. Are you my roommate?"

"Yes, I'm Oliver Wolcott. Is there a candle here that I can light?"

Noah got up and lit one of Ma's homemade candles. By the dim light, Oliver unpacked his clothing. He blew out the flame and crawled into the empty bed.

"Sorry I woke you," Oliver said. "We had a long trip. I thought I'd never get here." He turned over in bed. "I'll see you in the morning."

"Goodnight," Noah answered. Wide awake now, he thought of his first day in school back in West Hartford. He remembered how eager he was. *I can't wait for tomorrow. I wonder if I have everything I need?* In his mind, he checked off his supplies. *Quill pens. Ink. Paper.*

At the first sound of the six o'clock rising bell, Noah jumped out of bed. *I wonder why I didn't hear the roosters? I have to milk the cows.* Then he remembered where he was. *New Haven. Yale College.* Looking toward the other bed, he saw that his roommate still slept.

"Wake up, Oliver," Noah called. "You don't want to be late your first day of school."

Rubbing his eyes, Oliver slowly crawled out of bed. After dressing, the boys went to chapel for prayers. Breakfast was at 7:30. When they finished, they hurried to their first class.

"Hey freshies, run and get my books from my room," an upperclassman yelled. "Hurry and bring them here."

"We're not your slaves," Noah said. He wasn't used to being ordered around by anyone but Pa.

"Oh, yes you are, smarty. You're a freshman aren't you?"

"Yes, but my grandfather was governor of Connecticut and I don't plan to be anybody's slave," Noah bragged.

The older boy laughed. "You'll get the pride knocked out of you before long." He headed back toward his dormitory.

"Was your grandfather really governor?" Oliver asked as they continued down the path.

"No," admitted Noah, "it was my great-great-great-grandfather, John Webster, back in 1656. It just sounded better to say he was my grandfather."

In class, the boys were seated alphabetically. Noah sat next to Oliver when the tutor called out the names Webster and Wolcott.

At noon, the hungry boys hurried to the dining hall. Noah and Oliver joined the other freshmen sitting at long tables.

"Injun pudding today," Oliver said, as he looked at the cornmeal floating in broth in the serving bowl before them.

"With turnips," Noah added.

After prayer, the boys passed the cider around. They all drank in turn from the same pewter can.

"Look out," Oliver yelled, as a soggy piece of corn bread flew through the air and hit the wall behind his back. As the greasy stain spread, another piece of bread headed in their direction.

"Boys, stop throwing food," Dr. Daggett shouted from the raised platform where he sat with the other two teachers and the four tutors.

For a few minutes, the upperclassmen sat quietly. Then, ignoring the president, they started aiming food at the freshmen once again. Noah was amazed at the lack of respect. In his home, if he had done something like that, Pa would have taken him to the barn for a whipping faster than you could say "The redcoats are coming."

When the meal ended, the students were allowed several hours to exercise. Most of the boys went for a walk. Noah and Oliver with another freshman, Joel Barlow, decided to explore the town of New Haven. After a few times around the green and a trip to the waterfront, they returned to the campus. There wasn't much excitement in sleepy New England villages in 1774.

Three hours of study from three to six in the afternoon passed quickly for Noah. He enjoyed reading his textbooks and writing papers in Latin. The Greek lessons were the hardest.

Supper at six was plain brown bread and milk. "This tastes mighty good," Noah said to his new friend Joel. "We have the same thing for supper at home." The boys ate their meal while dodging more bread that was thrown at them. As soon as they finished, they went to their dormitory.

Back in their room, the main topic of conversation was the war with England. Oliver and Joel sat on the bed. Noah was too excited to sit.

"I wish I had been at that Boston Tea Party," he said. "Imagine dumping 342 chests of tea into the harbor."

"I'll bet the king was angry when he found out what happened to his precious tea," Joel said.

"Can't you just see Paul Revere and the men with him?" Noah crouched down, pretending that he was an Indian. "Almost a hundred of them dressed in blankets, feathers, and war paint, sneaking on the ships that night."

"Isn't it odd that no one stopped them," Oliver said.

"Would you stop a bunch of Indians dressed for war?"

"No, I guess I wouldn't," agreed Oliver.

"I heard that Mr. Revere left Boston that same night and rode hundreds of miles the next few days to let the rest of the colonies know what happened." Noah paused, then went on. "Those redcoats will find out that we won't pay taxes on their tea or anything else when we get through with them."

In February, the students of Yale began preparing for combat. They formed a militia company and drilled under the direction of two regular soldiers. Noah played the fife and led the group in marching practice. They learned to play a new tune one day. Noah told Oliver about it in their room that night.

"We learned a new marching song today," he said.

"What is it?" Oliver asked.

"It's called 'Yankee Doodle.' A British army doctor wrote the words to make fun of our American soldiers."

"I know that a doodle is a stupid fellow," Oliver said, "but what's a Yankee?"

"Yankee is the way the Indians pronounce the word *English*," Noah said. "The song is about one of our poorly dressed soldiers riding into town on a pony. A feather in his hair made him look like an Indian."

"Why do you play it if it makes fun of our army?"

"We heard that the Americans have taken it up as their marching song. It backfired on the British." He put his fife to his lips. "Listen to the tune."

"That's a lively one. I like it," Oliver said when Noah finished playing the song.

On April 21, the boys in chapel listened breathlessly as Dr. Daggett spoke. "About 800 soldiers left Boston to march to Concord, eighteen miles away," he told them. "War has come. The Americans are fighting the British."

Great excitement swept over the campus. Everyone talked about the war. "Did you hear about Paul Revere's signal to the colonists?" Noah asked his roommate on their way to the buttery.

"Yes. One lantern hung in the church steeple if the British were coming by land."

"And two if by sea," added Noah.

Noah continued, "I like what our men said at Lexington."

"What?"

"Don't fire unless fired upon. But if they mean to have a war, let it begin here!" Noah got excited just talking about it. "Maybe now the government in England will know that we meant what we said."

"Do you mean 'no taxation without representation'?"

"Right," Noah said. "We'll show those redcoats that we mean business. If Pa hadn't paid a lot of money to keep me in college, I'd join the Army right now."

One warm June evening, General George Washington rode into New Haven to spend the night. He was on his way to Boston to lead the American Army. The next morning, the Yale fife-and-drum corps, led by Noah Webster, marched to the house where the General was staying. The boys went through their drill and played "Yankee Doodle" for him.

Noah couldn't keep his eyes off the General. What a man! He was tall with large hands and feet. He wore a dark blue coat with buff waistcoat and breeches, white stockings, and black shoes. There was a vital strength about him that made him stand out from the others in his group. Dignity and honesty shone from his smiling blue eyes.

When the boys finished playing, General Washington headed on to Boston to take command of the army camped near the city.

The next month, college classes were canceled because of the war. Noah went home to West Hartford.

6
The War Years

June 1776

"Listen to this, Pa." Noah read from the newspaper, "Our delegates from Connecticut voted to substitute 'God Save the United Colonies' for 'God Save the King'."

The two men sat at the breakfast table discussing the war news. Noah read on. "Thomas Jefferson, John Adams, Benjamin Franklin, Roger Sherman, and Robert Livingstone have been appointed to prepare a declaration of independence. Now isn't that something!"

"Yesterday I heard that a Board of War has been appointed, too," Pa said. "But we better get at the chores. It's half past five and the cows aren't milked. Now that Abram's married and gone there's extra work to do around here."

By eight o'clock in the evening Noah was ready to go to bed. As soon as family worship ended, he and Charles climbed the stairs and went to the south chamber.

With his college books piled beside the bed, Noah often read until dark and fell asleep reading. He didn't always remember crawling into bed.

The smell of frying ham woke him in the morning. *It's good to be back to Ma's cooking.*

There wasn't much time for games that summer, but one evening Noah went to a husking bee with Charles.

The young men and women sat in a circle in the yard, shucking ears of corn. The rules they followed said that if a boy found a red ear, he could kiss the girls. If a girl husked one, she picked a boy to kiss. When a girl discovered a bad ear, she was allowed to use it to whack the boy sitting next to her.

Noah was seated beside his friend Sarah when it happened. With an impish look, she took the ear of corn and hit him. "Ouch," he yelled. The side of his head stung, but his feelings hurt more than his head. *Why did I have*

*to be next to Sarah when she found the rotten
ear? I wanted her to find a red one.*

The evening ended with singing around an
open fire. Crickets added to the music with
their cheerful chirping. The moon was high and
white. As the stars came out one by one, Noah
thought he would ask Sarah if he could walk
her to her home. Just as he turned toward her,
he heard his name being called.

"Noah," Charles yelled, "are you ready to go
home?" Noah had forgotten that he rode over
with his younger brother.

"I suppose I can leave," he said. "Get the
horse and we'll go." He looked at Sarah. She
was already laughing and talking with another
boy.

All the way home, Charles talked about the
events of the evening. He chuckled. "It sure
was funny to see you get whacked by Sarah.
Your face turned as red as an apple."

"Be quiet," his brother snapped. "I don't
want to hear any more about it."

"Well, what bit you?" Charles asked.

"Nothing," Noah said. "I said I don't want
to talk about it." The boys rode home through
the quiet countryside with not a word spoken
except an occasional command to the horse.

Arriving home, Noah climbed the stairs
without speaking to anyone. Inside his room,
he sat on the edge of the bed.

"What's wrong with Noah?" Ma asked. "He didn't even say good night."

"He's upset because Sarah whacked him with a rotten ear of corn," Charles said. "I think he wanted her to give him a kiss."

"Never mind what you think," Noah yelled down the stairs. "It's none of your business." Closing the door, he prepared for bed while the rest of the family read the Bible and prayed.

****

Back at Yale for his second year of college, Noah found everyone talking about the war. Many students had joined the army. Those who were left on campus marched and drilled nearly every day.

When spring came, Noah got word that his brother Abram's wife had died while giving birth to a baby boy. The infant died too. After his wife's death, Abram enlisted in the American Army and marched to Montreal. Captured by the British, he was released when he came down with the dreaded disease, smallpox. A French-Canadian woman nursed him back to health, and he made his way home to the farm in West Hartford.

Noah and his family were thrilled to hear about the signing of the Declaration of Independence by John Hancock and others of the Second Continental Congress on July 4, 1776.

"America is going to be a free country," Noah said. "I wish I could help fight the British."

"You're going to stay in school and finish your studies," Pa told him.

In early August, college was dismissed when many of the students were sick with typhoid fever. This disease with high temperatures and headaches caused death in many cases.

Noah rushed home. Running into the house, he called out, "Where's Abram?"

"He's out in the barn with your Pa and Charles," Ma answered. "Can you say hello to your mother?"

"I'm sorry, Ma. I am glad to see you but I need to talk to Abram." He bolted out the side door and dashed to the barn.

"I'm going back with you when you rejoin your company," he told Abram. "College is out because so many are ill."

"Fine," Abram said. "We'll leave as soon as I get my strength back."

By the end of the month, when Abram was well enough to travel, Noah went with him back to his company which was camped in New York near Lake Champlain.

Noah and the other men set up their tents in the woods. Puddles of stagnant water stood in the low areas. Mosquitoes buzzed around Noah's face and neck.

The first night, no one slept well. Noah just got to sleep when he heard the familiar humming sound. Slapping his face and arms, he tried to kill the pesky insects in the dark. The tent was full of them. Bullfrogs from a nearby pond added to the confusion with their constant croaking. Noah was still awake when the morning light filtered through the canvas of his tent.

The second night, the men started smudge pots to keep the mosquitoes away. Smoke filled the tents.

"How can a fellow sleep with this miserable smoke?" Noah asked.

"Would you rather be eaten alive by mosquitoes?" said Abram.

"No, but I can't breathe with all this smoke. I don't know which is worse, smoke or mosquitoes."

Abram looked with disgust at his brother. "If you're going to be a man, you'll have to learn to put up with some discomfort."

After a brief time with his brother, Noah returned to college for his third year.

"How was life in the army?" Oliver asked, as they prepared for bed the first night after Noah's return.

"We didn't see any redcoats," Noah said, "but we sure saw the mosquitoes. They were worse than the British."

Yale was so crowded that Noah and Oliver shared their room with two other boys. Food was scarce. Farmers cut cornstalks and crushed them in cider mills. Boiling the juice to a syrup, they made a substitute for sugar. The students were dismissed in early December because of the food shortage. Noah went home not feeling well.

When he walked in the door of the old farmhouse, Mother gave him a hug. "My, you feel hot!" she said. She felt his forehead.

"You're burning up, young man. Go up to your bed and I'll send Pa after the doctor."

"My head and back ache too," Noah said. "I feel sick all over."

The doctor came that evening. After examining Noah, the doctor said, "He has smallpox. It's very contagious. Many people who have it are dying." He looked at the rest of the family who were gathered around. "The rest of you must stay away from him as much as possible."

In three days, Noah broke out with a rash. Small dark red spots covered his body. Blisters, the size of peas, formed on these spots.

All through the month of December, Noah was a critically sick young man. He slept in the parlor so that his mother could take care of him without climbing the stairs. Weeks went by.

The blisters became scabs. Noah thought the itching would never stop. Finally one day he felt well enough to sit up on a chair and read a book.

"Our prayers are answered," Ma told the rest of the family at the supper table that night. "I believe our Noah is going to live."

After his long illness, Noah returned to college when the students were called back in January.

One day Noah, with about twenty-five of his classmates, walked out of chapel just as the service was beginning.

"What are you boys doing?" Mr. Buckminster asked.

"We're protesting the unfair punishment of two of our classmates," one of the students answered.

"What happened?"

"Dr. Daggett made them go without eating for two days because they were fighting. We're not going back to chapel until the president apologizes to them."

After dinner, the protestors were called into the president's office. "I am shocked at what happened today," Dr. Daggett said. "You have a choice of making a public confession of your wrongdoing or be punished."

That evening, the boys gathered in the dormitory. Noah suggested that as a group they should admit they were wrong and confess it in chapel.

The boys thought it over. They made their decision. During chapel the next day, Noah and the others went in front of the rest of the students and apologized for walking out of chapel the day before.

"We were wrong," their spokesman said. "We promise to never do it again."

Noah was embarrassed. "I hope my parents don't hear about this," he said to Oliver, as they walked to their class.

"I think they'll be proud of you for helping the group decide to apologize," Oliver said.

There was much unrest on campus. Food shortages and the war with England made everyone tense.

"I'm sorry, men, but we have no more food," the president announced again in March. "You must return to your homes." The students left.

"I'm home again, Ma," Noah said, as he walked into the farmhouse kitchen. "What's for supper?" He gave her a hug.

"We're having dandelion greens and brown bread," Mother said.

"Not dandelions," Noah groaned. "That's about all we've eaten at college this spring."

"Things have been hard here, too, son. Be thankful for the greens. It could be worse." She looked at her skinny son. "I'll try to fatten you up while you're home."

The students returned to school in a few weeks. That spring, Dr. Daggett resigned. Few of the students missed him when he left. The lack of discipline and leadership in the college needed to be changed.

A new president, Dr. Ezra Stiles, was chosen. All the boys liked him. He was very strict, but fair. He knew how to praise as well as criticize. The food shortage, combined with respect for the new president, brought an end to the throwing of food in the dining hall.

War came closer. British General Burgoyne, spreading terror throughout north-

eastern New York and Vermont, planned to cut
off New England and New York from the rest of
the colonies. In every Connecticut town, the
militia went to help the American troops along
the Hudson River. Noah's father, now a captain, drilled the Hartford men. They prepared
to head for Albany.

Noah left Yale in September to join the
militia. He, along with his father and brothers,
went up the east bank of the Hudson. Across
the mighty river, the town of Kingston could be
seen in flames.

Before reaching Albany, the volunteers
were met by a messenger waving his sword in
triumph and shouting, "Burgoyne is taken!
Burgoyne is taken!" The British general had
been forced to surrender.

Captain Webster and his group turned
around and headed for home, thankful that
they didn't have to fight. On the trip back, they
slept on beds of straw in barns and sheds along
the road.

"We're home, Ma," Noah shouted, as they
neared the homestead. Mistress Webster
bustled about the kitchen cooking potatoes and
baking bread for the hungry men. "Did you
fight the British?" she asked.

"No, they surrendered before we got there,"
Noah said. "I didn't even see a redcoat, let
alone fight one." He looked at his mother.

"How did you get along with the farm while we were gone?"

Ma smiled. "With the strength that God gave us, Jerusha and I did all the chores and brought in the harvest while you men were away. Mercy came over to help us several times." She sighed. "I'm mighty glad to have you all back, safe and sound. God is good."

The next day, Noah went back to New Haven. The now familiar road didn't seem nearly as long as the first time he had walked it with Pa.

In Noah's last year of college, only the seniors were on campus because of the food shortage and war. They, too, were sent home in February. Young Noah went home to help on the farm during this time. In between spring plowing and planting, he studied the books that he brought home from Yale.

One evening in late June, the family sat down at the supper table. New potatoes and fresh peas from the garden filled the platters. Light from the setting sun streamed through the kitchen window. Noah looked around the table. Only Jerusha and Charles were home now. Abram and his new bride, Dolly, lived nearby. Mercy also lived in West Hartford with her family. Soon it would just be Charles at home, since Jerusha planned to marry Joel Lord in November.

Noah was eager to get back to college to finish his schooling. As much as he loved his family, he felt more at home in the classroom now.

"Did you hear about your friend Sarah?" Charles asked as he ate his applesauce.

"What about her?" Noah's face turned red.

"She's going to marry Daniel Gilbert."

A big lump came into Noah's throat. He wanted to leave the room, but didn't. "So what about it?" he said, trying to act as if he weren't interested.

Charles looked closely at Noah. "I thought you'd want to know. You always were sweet on her."

Noah changed the subject. "I'll be leaving soon to finish my final classes and have examinations," he said. "Will any of you be able to come and see me graduate?"

"We can't all leave," Pa said. "The cows have to be milked and someone has to feed the animals. But I plan to ride to New Haven to be there for your graduation."

Noah excused himself and went up to the south chamber. He lay on the bed. *So Sarah is getting married. I can't believe it.* The ache inside his chest didn't go away until he finally fell asleep.

On September 9, 1778, Noah Webster, Junior, was chosen to give a speech in the college chapel. His proud father sat with other parents and teachers as Noah, along with his classmates, received the degree of Bachelor of Arts.

Back home in West Hartford, Noah read in the newspaper about the British invasion of New Haven. The article told how volunteers from the college tried to keep them away. They failed. Former president Dr. Daggett, then in his seventies, fired at the British with a rusty old gun. Captured by the redcoats, he was forced to march more than five miles, robbed, stabbed, and beaten. He never recovered from his injuries and died in the following year.

Noah felt sad to think of an old man being treated so badly. "I'd like to chase all the redcoats back to England," he said. But as much as he loved his country, Noah knew that others were better at fighting. He could best serve America by using his education to help others. *Lawyer? Teacher? Which should I be?* Noah decided that he wanted to be a lawyer.

7
The Schoolmaster

September 1778

Twenty-year-old Noah was a college graduate without a job. One afternoon his father
called him into the parlor.

"Take this," he said, handing his son an
eight-dollar bill. "You must now seek your
living; I can do no more for you."

Noah looked at the almost worthless bill. Eight dollars in continental money was worth about two dollars in silver.

"Is that all you have?" he stammered.

"I'm afraid it is," said Father. "I really would like to help you, but I have no more money. You're on your own from now on."

Noah thanked his father and headed to his room. "Don't look for me at supper time. I won't be eating," he called down the stairs.

For three days and nights, Noah stayed in his room. He sat for hours, staring at the floor. *What can I do?* he wondered. *I wanted to study to be a lawyer, but I have no money.* He went without food and spent the time reading books and thinking about his problem.

When Charles came to the room the first evening, Noah was reading.

"What's the book?" Charles asked.

"Dr. Johnson's *Rambler*."

Charles peered over Noah's shoulder. "Isn't he the one who wrote the dictionary in England?"

"He's the one," Noah said. "He says a lot of helpful things in this book."

Charles looked puzzled. "Why are you staying in the room and going without eating?"

Noah was silent for a minute. He looked up. "When you have to make a decision that affects your whole life, you need to be alone and spend your time thinking about it."

"I don't understand you," Charles said. "But I hope you can get a job and make a living."

Noah turned back to his book while Charles prepared for bed. He read long after Charles went to sleep.

On the third morning, Noah made a decision. *I'll teach school until I have enough money to study law.*

Noah came out of his room and joined the rest of the family at the breakfast table.

"I'm going to apply for a teaching job," he told them.

"Good." Ma sighed with relief. "You'll be a fine teacher."

"It's about time you earned some money," Charles said. "The rest of us did without so you could go to college."

"That's enough, Charles," Pa said. "Let's forget the past and look ahead." He looked around the room. "We have much for which to be thankful. We have food on the table, a good sturdy house, and clothing on our backs."

"Yes, God is good," Mother added. "Let's not complain."

Charles left the table. "Noah always gets the best," he muttered as he headed out the front door.

Noah got a job for the winter term teaching in Glastonbury. Some of his pupils were almost his age. The one-room building was crowded and cold. Those near the fire roasted. The ones away from it shivered. Noah tried to put the desks where all the children could be comfortable.

Schoolmaster Webster didn't believe in beating his pupils to make them learn. Most teachers kept a stick on their desk. If a child didn't know the answer to a question, the teacher gave him a hard whack and sent him to his seat. There was no stick on Noah's desk. Instead, he offered rewards for good work.

"If you get all your answers right today, we'll have an extra half-hour of play outside," he announced one morning. Nearly everyone had a perfect paper that day. Recess time came. Noah went outside with his pupils.

The children gathered around their young teacher. "What would you like to play today?" asked Noah.

"Crack the Whip," shouted the boys.

"Tag," yelled the girls.

Noah chuckled. "We'll play both. Grab hands for Crack the Whip." He took the head position and swung the line. When he suddenly stopped, the children on the outside flew to the ground. They sat and watched as the game continued. When the last child lost his grip and fell, Noah said, "Let's play Tag." His ruddy cheeks and bright eyes made him look as young as some of his students.

After playing Tag until all were panting, they trooped inside together. Noah joined the children in the long line waiting for the dipper at the water bucket.

"That was fun, Mr. Webster," said one of the boys.

"Just wait until we have a spelling bee. You'll really enjoy that," responded Noah.

Mr. Webster introduced spelling bees and other games to help his students learn words and facts. That afternoon, the teacher divided the room into two teams. Each side chose a captain. Lined up on either side of the classroom, one by one the members of the teams sat down when they missed a word. Excitement grew as the two best spellers in the school faced each other.

"Responsibility," announced the schoolmaster.

"Responsibility," repeated the girl who was standing. "R-e-s-p-o-n-s-a-b-i-l-i-t-y." Each member of her team held his breath as they waited for Noah to say if it was right or wrong.

"Incorrect," said Mr. Webster. The opposing team cheered as the defeated speller sat down.

The teacher turned to the lone boy standing. "Responsibility," he pronounced. The boy stuck his tongue in his cheek and looked at the ceiling. With eyes closed he slowly repeated, "Responsibility. R-e-s-p-o-n-s." He hesitated as all eyes looked at him. The room was as quiet as a schoolhouse at midnight. After a pause, he went on, "i-b-i-l-i-t-y."

"Correct," said Mr. Webster with a smile. A mighty cheer went up as the winning team clapped their hands for their champion speller.

With the excitement of games and rewards, the children worked hard to please their young schoolmaster. The year ended in a flurry of examinations, report cards, and goodbyes.

The next fall, Noah moved back home to teach in the little schoolhouse in West Hartford.

Noah's mother looked puzzled when he brought books to the supper table. "What is this, Noah?" she asked. "Are you going to eat your books as well as read them?"

"I'm sorry, Ma," he replied. "I don't mean to be rude. But I *must* read and learn as much as I can. I have so many books in my head. I have to get them written."

"What is your big rush?" she asked.

"There is almost nothing in my schoolroom for the boys and girls to read that's written by Americans," he said. "The books we had when I was a child are still there. It looks like I'll have to write something for them myself."

Ma looked thoughtful. "Perhaps you are the one to do it. I pray that God will guide you in your plans. You have always loved words. Maybe this is your chance to use them to help others."

Walking back and forth to school each day, Noah thought about the need for a new spelling book. Next year I'll start writing it, he promised himself.

****

In January, the snow was so deep that it covered the fences. The young schoolmaster left the house in early morning to try to get the old school building warm before the children arrived.

After carrying in wood and starting a fire in the fireplace, Noah looked around the room. The schoolhouse was in worse shape than it had been when he was a pupil. The same old tables stood in the room, too high for the younger children and too low for the older ones. Initials carved in the tops made the surface rough for writing. Nothing on the walls. No shelves. No storage cupboards.

Everyone still drank water from the same bucket. Noah often wondered if that could be why so many of the youngsters were often sick. If one caught a cold, several others came down with it.

He shivered in the cold room. Air came through the cracked windows and thin walls. Blasts of wind rattled the building. *Why don't parents do something about improving the schools?* Noah's thoughts were gloomy.

Taking a broom from the corner, he vigorously swept the dirt floor. The ice in the water bucket was starting to melt. Sprinkling some water on the floor helped to settle the dust.

"Good morning, Mr. Webster."

"Hello, Ruth. You're early today."

"Pa brought me in the cutter on his way to the blacksmith shop."

"Well, since you're here early, you can help me tidy up the room," Mr. Webster said.

Ruth found a rag and dusted the tables and benches. She rinsed the dipper and placed it by the bucket.

By the time they had the room cleaned, most of the children were inside. Puddles of melted snow formed under the wooden pegs where wet coats and hats hung. The smell of damp wool mingled with smoke from the fireplace.

Reading, ciphering, and spelling classes passed quickly. Older pupils helped younger ones while Mr. Webster worked with those who needed special help. One of the boys carried wood inside several times to feed the fire. Each time the door was opened, the children shook with cold.

"Get your dinner pails. It's time to eat," the teacher announced at noon.

The children quickly huddled around the fire to eat their corn bread and dried apples. Their teacher sat with them, eating the bread and cold succotash that his mother had packed for him. They drank water from the dipper shared by everyone.

After eating, the children went outside to play fox and geese in the snow. Noah watched from the window. A giant circle was made. Tramping the snow with their feet, the children formed spokes inside the circle until it looked like a wheel. The child who was the fox chased up and down the spokes until he caught one of the geese. When he caught someone, that person became the fox. Noah smiled as he remembered playing the game when he was a child at this same school. *I'd like to be out there with them, but I have work to do.* A brisk wind was driving gray clouds across the sky. Noah went to his desk to check his ink supply for the goosequill pens.

"It looks like I'll have to make more ink tonight," he said aloud. "I hope Ma has some walnuts left."

Brown ink was made by mashing and boiling walnut or butternut hulls with vinegar and salt added. For black, he added soot from the chimney.

Noah put another log on the fire. The room was getting colder. The old building creaked. A dash of sleet, like a warning, pelted the glass. It must be getting worse outside. He looked out the window. Snow swirled across the school grounds. Clouds hung low overhead. Gusty winds piled snow up against the side of the building and howled around the corner.

"I'd better ring the bell," he said.

The children rushed inside when they heard the bell. Red noses and icy hands and feet gradually thawed as they crowded around the fire. Puddles of melted snow made the dirt floor turn to mud.

"We're going to dismiss early," Noah told his pupils. "It looks like we're in for another blizzard. I want you to go right home. Don't dilly-dally along the way."

After the children were gone, Noah straightened the room and banked the fire. He put on his overcoat and headed into the biting wind. Books went under his coat. Pulling his woolen muffler up over his chin, Noah felt the snow beat against his face. With his coat whipping around his legs, he plodded through drifts of snow up to his knees.

The last 100 yards up the ridge seemed endless. Several times he stumbled and fell. Once, his beloved books dropped. Noah groped around in the snow. Wiping them off, he tucked them carefully under his coat again. Finally, he opened the door of the house and stepped inside.

"Anybody here?" he yelled. Stamping the snow off his shoes before going any farther, Noah called again, "Ma, I'm home." He heard the whir of the spinning wheel upstairs in the north chamber.

Climbing up the stairs, he yelled again, "I'm home."

Mother was spinning wool into yarn, feeding the short fibers into the spinning wheel. While twisting them, she held them tight. She looked up as he climbed the last step. "You're home early."

"Yes. It's a blizzard out there. I'm thankful to be inside." Noah went downstairs with his mother following him. He walked over to the fireplace in the kitchen and warmed his hands. "What's in the pot?"

"I'm cooking beans for supper," Mother said. "Did you see Pa and Charles outside? They went to check on the livestock a few minutes ago."

"No, I didn't see anything but snow," Noah said. "I'll go look in the barn."

Putting his coat on, he headed in the direction of the barn. Blowing snow filled his tracks as soon as he made them. Lost in a cloud of white, he hoped he was going in the right direction. "I should be there by now," he said.

"Pa, Charles, Halloo." The wind carried his voice back to him. Turning to the right, he bumped into the hay wagon. "I must be behind the barn," he muttered. Noah turned around and headed into the biting snow again. Bang. He hit his head on the side of a building. Feeling his way along the rough boards, he finally reached the barn door. Inside, the whitefaced cows turned and looked at him. But there was no sign of Pa or Charles anywhere.

Heading back to the house, Noah tried to think where they might be. He didn't dare to start looking for them on foot.

Just as he reached the door, he heard the sound of sleigh bells. Pa brought the horse to a halt beside the house. Charles sat on the seat of the cutter beside his father. "We went to pick you up at school," Pa said. "When I saw this storm coming, I knew you couldn't make it walking."

"Well, I did," Noah said. "I dismissed school early. You must have left after I got home. I was inside talking to Ma and didn't hear you leave." He laughed. "Thank you for trying to rescue me. I went out to the barn to rescue you."

"Thank the good Lord that you're home," Pa said. "I was really worried when we didn't see you anywhere." He flicked the reins, heading the horse toward the barn, as Noah went into the warm kitchen.

8
The Writer

June 1781

"Noah Webster, Junior, Esquire, Attorney at Law. My, that sounds good," Noah said, reading it aloud from his paper. Noah was now living with a lawyer friend, in Litchfield, Connecticut, but he found that a new address and a fancy title didn't get him any jobs.

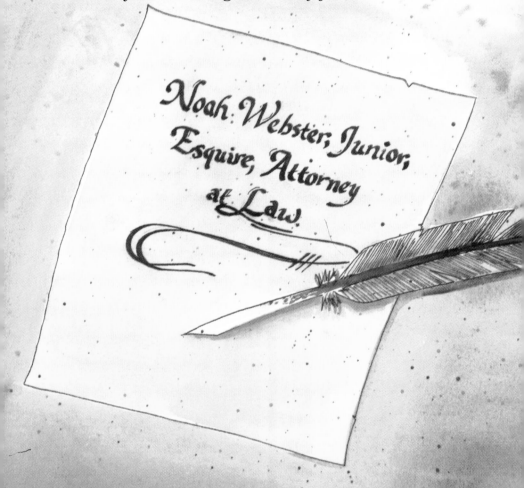

He had studied night and day. Mastered all the law books in his friend's library. Passed the examination to become a lawyer. Still no job. Noah decided to return to teaching.

The Revolutionary War continued. New York City was captured by the British. People fled from there to Sharon, Connecticut, on the eastern border of New York State. Noah moved to Sharon to open a school of his own. Putting an ad in the newspaper, he stated that he would teach young ladies and gentlemen for nine shillings per student.

The school opened in the summer. Schoolmaster Webster taught reading, writing, literature, geography, vocal music, and the English language.

In September, Noah Webster received the degree of Master of Arts from Yale College in honor of his writing and speaking.

Noah started an evening singing school in Sharon. Slicking down his bushy red hair, he stooped to look at his reflection in the steel mirror in the rented room where he stayed. Gray eyes, under overhanging eyebrows, stared back at him. *Not too bad looking*, he thought. One of his pupils, a beautiful young lady, agreed. Her name was Rebecca Pardee.

"May I see you home tonight?" Noah asked, after the other students left their night class.

"Oh, Mr. Webster, that is thoughtful of you," Rebecca said.

They walked down a quiet street under a full moon. "You have a lovely voice," Noah said. He wanted to tell her that he loved her but felt it wasn't the right time.

One night Noah invited Rebecca to go for a ride in his buggy. The horse clip-clopped along the dirt road as Noah guided it toward a nearby pond.

"Whoa, Nellie," he said, drawing the reins tight. The mare stopped beside the water. Gentle ripples followed the white path of the moonlight across the pond. Beside the peaceful water, Noah slipped his arm around Rebecca's waist. "You are a lovely lady," he whispered. "I've been wanting to ask you something for some time." Rebecca didn't answer.

Noah took a deep breath and blurted out the question, "Will you marry me?"

Rebecca was silent. She sat looking at the silver spot the moon made on the surface of the pond. Noah saw a troubled look come across her face. "I don't know," she said, gently shaking her head. "My friend, who is a major in the army, has also asked me to marry him."

Rebecca Pardee couldn't make up her mind which man she wanted to marry. She asked her family what to do. They could not decide either, so they took it to the leaders of the church. The church elders decided in favor of the army officer.

The disappointed young schoolmaster closed his school in early October and packed his belongings to move home.

In Connecticut, he rode past the familiar haystacks and fields of rye. Stone fences lined the way. Maples and sumac tried to outdo each other in brilliant color. Here and there, an evergreen provided the green yarn which tied together God's colorful patchwork quilt. The sun was dropping low in the west when Noah reached Hartford.

As he reached the village, Noah remembered the story of the towering oak tree in Hartford which once hid the charter that granted Connecticut the power to govern itself.

Sir Edmund Andros was appointed by England's King James the second to be governor-in-chief of all New England. On All Hallows Eve, October 31, 1687, he had arrived in Hartford accompanied by a troop of seventy soldiers.

The militia and the governor of Connecticut colony gave him a proper military welcome. Andros met with the Connecticut men at the inn across the green. After dinner, Andros demanded the charter. Governor Treat didn't want to give it up but finally had to produce it.

The precious document lay on the table. One of the older men, who had been ill for some time, got up to speak about how much they

wanted to keep their charter. Suddenly, he fell
forward, knocking over the candles. The room
was in darkness. By the time the candles were
lighted again, the charter was gone.

According to the story, the charter was
handed in the darkness to a young captain of
the militia, Joseph Wadsworth. Stepping
quickly through an open window, the captain
evaded the English soldiers and made his way
to the home of Samuel Wyllys, one of the original guardians of the charter.

The great oak tree that stood in front of the
Wyllys home was old even then. And hollow.
Captain Wadsworth wrapped the charter in his
tunic. After thrusting it deep into the hollow of
the great oak, he ran off into the night.

Connecticut submitted to the government
of Sir Edmund Andros as they were forced to
do. But they did not surrender their charter.

Thinking of the ancient oak tree, Noah was
proud that he was a native of Connecticut. It
was good to be back home.

"Noah, what a surprise," Mother Webster
said as her son came through the farmhouse
door. "My, but you're so thin. Have you been
eating properly?"

"I'm home to stay, Ma," Noah said, as he
gave her a hug. "My school didn't work out."
He didn't tell her about being jilted by Rebecca.
It still hurt too much to talk about it.

"Have you heard the news about the war?" Pa asked.

"Yes, I heard that the British surrendered at Yorktown."

Pa joined in, "And the colonies are free."

"Hooray!" Noah couldn't contain his joy. Throwing his hat into the air, he shouted, "We're Americans at last. No more taxes from Great Britain." In spite of his sorrow over the loss of a ladyfriend, Noah was happy. The war was over. "I'll do everything that I can to help our new country," he said. "We need books written in America by Americans."

Noah spent the remainder of the fall and winter months resting his nerves and hunting for a job to earn some money. He still owed his parents for his schooling at Yale. Studying French, Italian, German, and Spanish, he kept his candle burning far into the night.

Besides learning new languages, Noah started writing a spelling book.

In the spring, twenty-four-year-old Noah crossed the Hudson River with 75 cents in his pocket and started a school in Goshen, New York.

After the school days ended, Noah worked on his book. He spent many hours writing. Instead of going to parties or visiting with friends, he sat at his desk and wrote every night until after midnight.

"I must get this book done for the school children," he declared. "All the school books come from England. They're written for children in Great Britain. I want American books for American children."

Noah Webster changed many words in his book so they would be spelled the way that he felt they should be spelled. The British wrote *honour* and *colour*. He dropped the letter *u* and spelled them *honor* and *color*. He made *wagon* out of *waggon* and *traveler* out of *traveller*. He dropped the last letter in some words: *Publick* and *musick* became *public* and *music*. Mr. Webster put in his own spellings for *jail, plow, draft,* and *ax* instead of the British *gaol, plough, draught,* and *axe*.

Besides spelling words, the book gave advice to children:

A wise child loves to learn his book; but the fool would choose to play with toys.

Sloth keeps such a hold of some clowns, that they lie in bed when they should go to school; but a boy that wants to be wise will drive sleep far from him.

Love him that loves his book, and speaks good words, and does no harm, for such a friend may do thee good all the days of thy life.

Be kind to all as far as you can; you know not how soon you may want their help.

If you want to be good, wise, and strong, read with care such books as have been made by wise and good men. Think of what you read in your spare hours. Be brisk at play, but do not swear; and waste not too much of your time in bed.

Noah included many proverbs:

When wine is in, wit is out.

A good cow may have a bad calf.

You must not buy a pig in a poke.

Let not your tongue cut your throat.

He that lies down with dogs must rise up with fleas.

The reading section in the back of the book began with four sentences of one-syllable words copied from the old book that Noah used when he was a boy:

No man may put off the law of God.

My joy is in His law all the day.

O may I not go in the way of sin.

Let me not go in the way of ill men.

The speller was completed in the summer of 1782. Noah tried it out with the parents of his students.

"It's wonderful," they all agreed. "There is nothing like it in America."

"I'm glad you like it," Noah said. "I've really worked hard on it. Too hard. In fact, I'm going to have to quit teaching if I'm going to keep writing books."

In August he went to Philadelphia to try to get recommendations for his book. Noah admired the city built on the banks of the Delaware River. He liked the neat red brick houses and the paved, well-lighted streets.

No one was interested in the speller. Noah was disappointed, but he didn't give up. He talked to schoolmasters and ministers. He tried to find a company to publish the book, but he found that no one wanted it.

Somewhat discouraged, Noah left Philadelphia and went back to Hartford. He talked to two of his friends who published a newspaper. They agreed to print the book if Noah would pay for the printing. Noah didn't have any money, so he went to see his old college friend, Joel Barlow.

"I'll lend you 500 dollars," Joel said. "I really believe the spelling book is important."

"Thank you," Noah said. "You are a good friend."

Because the printers put blue covers on the spelling book, people began to call it "The Blue-Backed Speller." It sold for 14 cents. The spellers were put in stores on shelves beside cheese, calico cloth, and peppermint candy.

School children liked Webster's spelling book. They enjoyed the stories. Grownups liked it, too. The 5,000 copies sold out, and more had to be printed.

Noah went to visit his parents one day. He was happy now because his dream of writing books was finally coming true.

"Ma," he said, "my spelling books are even going out West in covered wagons. Just think," he continued, "they are crossing mountains, rivers, and plains."

"I'm proud of you, son," his mother said. "I believe that God is helping you. Always give Him the praise." She paused, looking carefully at him. "Don't think too highly of yourself, Noah."

"I'll try to be humble, Ma, but isn't it wonderful how well my speller is selling? People say it's the most important book in the world, next to the Bible."

Mother Webster sighed. "I've heard that too," she said, "but it will never be as great as the Bible, even if it sells millions of copies."

As more and more copies of the speller were printed, there were millions of copies sold. Noah made changes and added new parts. Short stories followed the lists of spelling words. Children were expected to spell aloud all the words in the list before reading the story. One of the favorite fables in the book was this one:

Of the Boy That Stole Apples

An old man found a rude boy upon one of his trees stealing apples, and desired him to come down; but the young saucebox told him plainly he would not. Won't you? said the old man, then I will fetch you down; so he pulled up some tufts of grass and threw at him; but this only made the youngster laugh, to think the old man should pretend to beat him down from the tree with grass only.

Well, well, said the old man, if neither words nor grass will do, I must try what virtue there is in stones, which soon made the young chap hasten down from the tree and beg the old man's pardon. Moral: If good words and gentle means will not re-claim the wicked, they must be dealt with in a more severe manner.

"We have to make more copies," the printer told Noah. "We're sold out." Thousands more copies were printed. They went fast. The printers made still more.

Other people began copying Webster's book, making a few changes in it and printing it as their own.

"Look at this," Noah said to his father one day. "Here is a spelling book printed under someone else's name."

Pa looked at the book. "Why, it's nearly the same as yours."

"There are no national copyright laws to protect what I've written," Noah said. "Anyone can copy it and put his own name to it."

Even though Noah was busy writing another book, he made a decision. "I'll travel to all the colonies and try to get copyright laws passed," he said.

"How can you afford to go on a trip like that?" Pa asked.

"Perhaps I can sell my books as I go from city to city," Noah said. "I'll also give lectures, trying to get people to be interested in having one central government."

"You have a lot of ambition, son," Pa said. "I pray that God will go with you and protect you over the many miles."

9

The Traveler

May 1785

Even though he was excited about his trip, Noah hated to leave Hartford. The little village of 300 houses on the west bank of the Connecticut River was the capital of the colony. Noah liked to escort young ladies to parties. Writing books and stories kept him busy.

Newspapers printed Noah's articles, but not everyone liked him. Some made fun of his books. Others didn't like his ideas about a central government. "Noah Webster is a sneaky, snaky, fainthearted Whig," wrote one man. Comments like this hurt Noah's feelings, but he kept writing.

New Hampshire

Boston

New York   Mass.

Hartford .

Conn.

New Haven .

Rhode Islan

New York City

Pennsylvania

New Jersey

Maryland

Delaware

Virginia   Maryland

North Carolina

South Carolina

Georgia

N

W   E

S

One balmy evening in May, Noah went to
visit his parents in West Hartford. Ma and Pa
were out in the garden planting potatoes. Ma
stood lost in thought, her sunbonnet lying beside her on the ground. She watched Noah ride
toward them. "My, doesn't he cut a fine figure,"
she said to her husband. Noah sat tall and slim
in the saddle. His reddish-brown hair shone
like copper in the setting sun. Dismounting his
horse, Noah came over to where his parents
stood.

"I came to say goodbye."

"What are you planning to do?" Ma asked.

Noah cleared his throat. "You know my
feelings that we need to elect a President and
Congress to represent and govern our thirteen
colonies."

"Yes," Pa said. "Are you going to give lectures about that?"

"I plan to do just that," Noah said. "In fact,
I'm leaving tomorrow morning. That's why I
came to say goodbye to my two favorite people
before I go out to conquer the world."

"Where are you going?" Ma asked. "Remember that the Scriptures tell us that pride
goeth before a fall." She smiled. "I hope you
don't have a fall."

"I'm heading south to talk to people about
my ideas and to try to get copyright laws
passed to protect my writing."

"Will you also sell your books?" Pa inquired.

"Yes," Noah said. "I've already sent a case ahead to Baltimore. If I sell enough of them, I can pay you back some of the money I owe for my college education."

"Do you have plenty of clean clothes?" said Ma.

Noah chuckled. "You sound like a mother. Yes, my saddlebags are packed with changes of clothing. And with more books," he added.

Ma shook her head. "You have a lot of ambition, son. Your Pa and I can't travel very far, but our prayers will go with you all the way."

When they parted, Noah went back to Hartford to finish his preparations. The next morning he mounted his horse and headed for the cities. During the next few weeks he visited New Haven, New York, Philadelphia, and Baltimore.

Noah decided to spend the summer in Baltimore, a bustling city of nearly 10,000 people. After locating a room, he toured the city on Sunday afternoon. He was shocked when he saw young men flying kites and playing games on Sunday. *They wouldn't do that in New England.*

The next day, Noah visited all the storekeepers, leaving copies of his books for them to sell. After placing an advertisement about his

books in the newspaper, he set out for Alexandria, Virginia, by stagecoach. With his baggage
placed on top of the coach, Noah sat inside with
two other passengers.

Six horses pulled the stagecoach over rough
roads. The jolting and bouncing finally caused
a breakdown. Noah was dismayed. "I'll have to
go back to Baltimore and rent a horse," he told
the driver.

Walking back to the city, lugging his bags,
took the rest of the day. The next morning,
Noah began a fifty-mile trip on horseback to
Alexandria to tell the people there about copyright laws.

The following day, Noah decided to visit
George Washington at Mount Vernon. Riding
through the rich cornfields and oak forests
along the Alexandria highway, he thought
about the last time he had seen General Washington. What a day that was! Noah remembered how proud he was to be playing the fife
as he led the Yale militia. *I wonder if the general will remember me?*

Noah left the highway and entered the
Mount Vernon property through a white gate.
Riding toward the house, he admired the flow-
ering shrubs. Giant magnolias, weeping wil-
lows, and mulberry trees towered toward the
sky. Hot dust rose from his horse's hoofs and
settled in a fine gray powder on his dark coat.

As Noah approached the circular drive which enclosed a grassy area on the west entrance of the house, he noticed a figure on horseback coming toward him. It was George Washington returning from his daily round of the farms.

The general wore a blue coat, black breeches, and riding boots. Noah was again impressed with the man's physical appearance. What a man! General Washington, sitting tall and erect on his gray horse, still looked like Commander-in-chief. His ice-blue eyes penetrated Noah.

"Come in, Mr. Webster," he said, after Noah introduced himself. When the men dismounted, a servant came and took the horses to a stable.

Noah and Mr. Washington walked through the wide passageway which led from the west entrance to the piazza facing the Potomac River. Noah was glad to sit down in the cool shade. He looked in wonder at the row of white pillars that reached from the ceiling to the flagstone floor of the porch. A black servant brought tall glasses of cold cider.

"Would you have dinner with us and spend the night?" Mr. Washington asked.

Noah was glad to accept the invitation. After riding for miles, he was tired and hungry. The corn bread he had carried in his saddle-bags was long gone.

Another servant appeared with Noah's saddlebags and led him to an upstairs bedroom. After the man left, Noah looked around. Bright yellow walls reflected the afternoon sun. Great clumps of roses standing in white jars filled the room with their fragrance. A four-posted ma-hogany bed with canopy above tempted Noah to lie down. Instead, he walked to the window and looked out.

The house sat on a high hill overlooking the river. At this point, where the Piscataway joined the Potomac, the river was wide. Noah estimated it to be nearly two miles across to the Maryland side. He had never seen such beauti-fully kept lawns and flower beds as he saw before his eyes.

After removing his dusty coat and changing into fresh clothing, Noah joined his host in the dining room. He carried a copy of his spelling book with him to show to General Washington. Another guest, Mr. Robert Pine, an artist employed to do family portraits, joined them.

"I'd like to have you meet my wife," General Washington said, as Martha entered the room. Noah saw a plump, short lady with a pleasing smile. Her blue satin dress was covered by a flowered apron. A gauze cap with blue bows sat on her head.

"Welcome to Mount Vernon, Mr. Webster," Mrs. Washington said as the young man bowed toward her.

Why, she's just as common and friendly as my own mother, Noah thought. *I feel like a member of the family.*

Noah noticed that the general's hair was freshly powdered and he had changed from riding clothes to a plain buff coat, white waistcoat, and brown breeches.

At Mrs. Washington's signal, they sat at the long mahogany table. Ivory table knives and forks lay beside blue and white china. Cut-glass dishes of pickles, cheese, almonds, and raisins were already at the table. Noah's mouth watered. His eyes lit up as the servants carried in platters full of baked ham and roast goose. Bowls of potatoes, green beans, and applesauce appeared. Snowy white cloths covered hot breads in the center of the table. After the meal, mince pies and pancakes were passed to the guests.

"Why don't we go into my library," the general suggested, when the meal was over. Noah was glad to get up and walk into the next room. Looking around, he saw rows of shelves filled with books. Walking over to read some of the titles, he saw that Shakespeare's works stood beside *Don Quixote, Robinson Crusoe,* and *Gulliver's Travels.* He noticed an old copy of *Pilgrim's Progress.* Seeing it brought back memories of Connecticut and his childhood. *I wish I could stay a month, just to read the many books,* he thought.

"Tell me about *your* books," George Washington said. "I've heard of your writing and teaching." Before Noah could answer, the general continued, "Here in Virginia, many men and women can't even write their own name."

Noah was shocked. "In New England, a schoolhouse stands beside almost every church," he said. "Everyone can learn to read and write. In fact, we have a law that says that every town of fifty or more families must have a grade school. Towns with 100 or more families have to start a high school as well."

Handing a copy of his spelling book to the general, Noah said, "This is the book I have written to be used in schools. Would you be willing to recommend it to your friends?"

General Washington took the book. He skimmed through it and handed it back to Noah. "I really can't do that," Mr. Washington said. "I'm not a good judge of school books, since I'm not a teacher."

The two men spent some time discussing the need of a central government. Even though he was disappointed that George Washington would not recommend his spelling book, Noah cheerfully joined in playing a game of whist that evening.

General Washington mentioned his need of a secretary and a tutor for little Nelly and Washington Custis, the grandchildren who lived at Mount Vernon.

That night in the yellow bedroom, Noah rolled and tossed on the bed. So many thoughts cluttered his mind. *I know I could enjoy living at Mount Vernon as the General's secretary and as a tutor. But I must continue my work of writing and lecturing.* The next day he left.

Back in Baltimore, Noah packed his trunk for a trip to Charleston, South Carolina. "The only way to get there from here is by boat," he was told.

Noah paid his fare on the sailboat *George.* They set sail under a gentle breeze, but soon inky clouds formed overhead. Some days the wind blew so strongly that Noah thought they would surely be swamped. Other days were so calm that they failed to make any progress.

When the boat docked at Norfolk, Virginia, he went ashore long enough to sell three dozen books. In his diary he wrote, "I ate cherries for the first time today and counted 200 to 300 brick houses."

Back on the water, the captain had a grave announcement one day. "All our fresh food is gone, and the water supply is low," he said. "Only two quarts of water are left for each person."

Noah was tired and thirsty. The trip seemed endless. To help with the food shortage, he fished. With a harpoon, he caught a dolphin. After boiling the fish with silver, as they did in those days to prove it wasn't poisonous, Noah and his companions had an excellent dinner.

In the evening, Noah fished again and harpooned a porpoise.

"It must weigh at least 200 pounds," said one of the men who helped Noah put a net around the huge mammal.

"Watch it," yelled another. "The rope broke."

As the men watched in dismay, the porpoise dropped back into the ocean and disappeared.

Noah looked over the rail of the sloop. "There goes our supper." Everyone went hungry that night.

Four days later, Noah caught a young shark. They had fresh food again that night. The dolphins and sharks that the men caught on the twenty-eight-day trip saved their lives.

Arriving in Charleston, Noah admired the beautiful homes and churches. He sold more books and, as usual, counted the houses.

The boat trip back to Baltimore took only eight days. Noah caught a shark and noted in his diary that a squall blew them along. Otherwise the trip was uneventful.

When he returned, Noah started a singing school in a church and gave lectures to earn some money. Riding in the city, he counted 1,950 dwelling homes in Baltimore, besides 150 stores and public buildings.

As he was returning to his room one bitter January night, Noah fell from his horse. Lying in the icy street with sharp pains shooting through his leg, Noah remembered his mother's telling him that pride goeth before a fall. *This kind of fall isn't what she meant, but it surely does knock out my pride.* He painfully crawled forward to gather up the books that had spilled on the ground. After the precious books were back in his saddlebags, he tried to mount the horse but couldn't make it into the saddle. Leading the horse by its halter, Noah limped along toward his room. He was lame for a week, but he did not let his injury keep him from visiting the young ladies who attended his singing school.

Noah took many trips on horseback to towns near Baltimore. In Williamsburg he counted 230 houses, in Petersburg 300, in Wilmington 400.

In May, Noah Webster, Junior, started back toward Hartford, after being away for over a year. On horseback, he forded swollen streams and rode miles through forests. When he reached New York City he counted 3,500 homes. Besides numbering the houses in towns where he traveled, Noah recorded the temperature. He was America's earliest census taker. All these facts were stored away for future use.

As Noah came into Connecticut, the rolling hills and sparkling ponds looked good to him after being gone so long. He rode to West Hartford and walked in the door of the old farmhouse.

"Welcome home, son," Mother Webster said. "You look weary."

"I've traveled many miles by horse, stage, boat, and foot." Noah smiled at his mother. "It's good to be back."

Eating dinner with his parents, Noah noticed the flecks of gray in their hair. They weren't young anymore.

"Your dried apple pie is mighty fine, Ma," Noah said. "There's nothing like it anywhere I went."

Looking around the kitchen, he saw few
changes. The corner cupboard had some new
dishes. Dried herbs and vegetables hung over
the fireplace. Ma and Pa still slept in the parlor in the same bed in which Noah was born.
Blue calico curtains hanging around the bed
gave them privacy. *It's not as fancy as Mount
Vernon, but I'm glad to be home,* Noah thought.

"I'm giving a lecture about education and
the English language at North Meeting House
tonight," Noah said. "Would you like to come
and hear me speak?"

"Some of our neighbors have complained
about your charging for your lectures," Pa said.
"They think they should have free tickets to
hear you speak."

"I'm only charging two shillings," Noah
said. "If they want to hear me, they can pay for
their tickets. The only ones getting free tickets
are you two and some men of influence at the
capital."

"They don't seem very happy about the idea
of charging admission," Pa said quietly. "I hope
there isn't trouble about it."

Mistress Webster put on her best linen
bonnet and bright red and blue print dress. As
he helped her into the buggy, Noah said, "I
declare, Ma, you're just as light on your feet as
ever." On the way to church, Noah told them
about his visit with George and Martha Washington.

"You should have seen their house, Ma. It's a mansion. And they have a regular village of houses for their slaves."

"Why do they need so many slaves?" Pa asked.

"They have such a big plantation that it takes nearly 200 slaves to run it. They grow tobacco, corn, and wheat."

"But surely it doesn't take that many people to care for the fields," Pa said.

"Oh, they're not all farmers," Noah said. "Some work as stonecutters, bricklayers, painters, shoemakers, tailors, bakers, gardeners, and anything else you can think of. I don't approve of slavery, but I will admit that Mr. Washington takes good care of his people."

A farm wagon rumbled past them. Pa waved to the men who rode on it. "I wonder where they're going?" he said.

"Tell us more about the plantation, Noah," Ma said.

"Behind the mansion is a spinning house where the women make cloth from wool and flax and cotton grown on the estate. There's a smokehouse, icehouse, bakery, and stables. It's a little town by itself."

Another carriage passed them, and again Pa recognized some of the neighbors.

When they arrived at the church, Noah

jumped down to help Ma get out so that she wouldn't trip on her long skirt. While Pa tied the horse to a hitching post, Noah found a seat in the church for his mother. Arriving at the platform, he looked over the crowd. Ma smiled up at him while Pa sat beside her with a proud look on his face.

Noah had just started speaking when suddenly a rock flew through the window. Glass went everywhere. Several ladies screamed. Noah kept talking. Crash! Another rock. People ran in panic. Noah left the platform and went outside.

"What's going on?" he asked. A gang of men gathered around him. Noah knew that several of them were men who lived near his parents.

"We don't like the idea of you charging admission," they yelled. "Why didn't you give us free tickets? Aren't we good enough?"

One of the church elders pushed his way through the crowd of men and came striding toward Noah. "We'll have to ask you to leave our property," he said. "You can't use it anymore. There's too much damage to our building."

Noah moved to a hall and finished his lecture. After it ended, he went to his rented room in Hartford and sat with his head in his hands. *I can't understand why the people in my own home town don't like me,* he thought. On Thanksgiving Day, Noah left Hartford. He wrote in his diary that night, "I leave Hartford, perhaps for life, to seek a living."

On the road again, Noah stopped to lecture at any town with enough people to fill a room. His subject: the English language.

In Boston, Dover, Portsmouth, and Newburyport, he spoke about the need for copyright laws.

James Madison praised his work and said that Noah Webster was responsible for the passage of a copyright law in Virginia.

Noah met with the presidents of almost every major American college, including Harvard, Dartmouth, and Yale. All had good words to say about him.

Wherever he lectured, Noah remembered his experience in Hartford. With his lesson learned well, he gave free tickets to the poor.

10
The Bachelor Takes a Wife

December 1786

Noah was out of money again. He felt he must write or explode, but writing paid very little. Working on a new edition of *The New England Primer*, Noah changed the old alphabet sentences. The first two now read:

A was an Apple pie made by the cook.

B was a Boy that was fond of his book.

The stories that Noah included taught lessons of obedience. In one of them, a boy fell asleep while weeding beets and a mouse bit his toe. The lad remembered that his father had told him that a mouse would never bite a boy when he was at work.

In New Haven, Noah lectured at Yale College. Dr. Stiles sat in the audience. Noah felt proud to know that his former college president had come to hear him speak.

In early December, Noah left New Haven and headed for New York City to look for work. He noticed dark clouds forming in the west. A snowstorm was coming. Riding in a sleigh pulled by a horse, he got as far as Stratford. After a warm meal at the Inn, he started out again. Drifted snow made the horse strain with all his might. At a four-foot drift, the sleigh upset and broke. Noah walked to Fairfield. After a short night's rest, he rose early. It was still snowing. Starting out at five o'clock in the morning with a second horse and sleigh, Noah huddled under lap robes as he faced the cold biting wind. Drifts covered the roads. Again the sleigh overturned, and Noah was buried in snow. He clawed his way out and continued on to Norwalk. *I wonder if I'm going to make it. I must keep going, though, if I'm going to find a job.* He left the horse and sleigh at Norwalk and walked to Stamford through the deep snow. For another day, Noah fought drifts, trudging on with his head bent into the wind. When he finally reached New York City, he found that there were no jobs available.

On Christmas Day, Noah set off for Philadelphia. After a long, cold ride on a borrowed horse, he arrived and rented a room.

Pulling his muffler closer around his neck to keep out the cold wind, Noah rode his horse up Market Street to Fourth. When he came to Franklin Court, he passed through the high arched passageway and rode over the cobblestones to an inner courtyard, where he saw the elegant brick house built by Dr. Franklin. Standing three stories high, with garret windows above, it was impressive to Noah. As he gazed at the lightning rods on top of the house, Noah was reminded of his childhood when his mother read about them in the almanack.

Noah dismounted and knocked at the front door, which was soon opened by a heavyset woman. Noah introduced himself and asked to see Mr. Franklin.

"I am Sally Bache, Mr. Franklin's married daughter," the lady said. "Come inside and warm yourself by the fire."

Closing the door, she continued, "Father is upstairs in his library. I'll tell him you're here."

While he waited, Noah looked around the spacious dining room. The table could easily seat twenty-four people. He walked toward the fireplace. Below the marble mantel was a cast-iron insert. Noah had heard of Franklin stoves, and he examined this one carefully. Mr. Franklin's invention was said to heat a house far more efficiently than did open-hearth fireplaces.

It was rumored that the Franklins had a heated bathtub which Benjamin had invented. Noah thought of the long process of heating water in kettles and filling their tin tub for baths. It would be wonderful to have a heated bath. Perhaps he could ask about it.

"Father will see you in the library," Mrs. Bache said, as she led the way upstairs.

The first thing that caught Noah's eye was the wall of books. Lined up from floor to ceiling was probably the largest private library in America. Then he saw the man sitting at a desk.

Eighty-year-old Benjamin Franklin stood up to greet twenty-eight-year-old Noah Webster. Thin gray hair, falling over his ears to his neck, topped Mr. Franklin's large head. Small wire-rimmed spectacles perched on a straight nose. His voice was low as he came forward.

"Noah Webster. I've heard of you. In fact, I read your book, *Sketches of American Policy*, with great interest. I like your suggestions for a constitution for our new government.

"Some make fun of me for my ideas," Noah said.

"Don't be surprised at that." The elderly man pursed his lips. "Any time you work for something good, you will have many against you. There is no gain without pain. Those things that hurt, teach you much."

He motioned toward a rocker. "Please sit down." Noah sat in the chair, but he couldn't keep his eyes off the wall filled with books.

"How many volumes do you have, Dr. Franklin?"

"More than 4,000. Would you like to see how I reach the upper shelves?"

"Yes, I would," Noah said, as he stood and walked toward the bookshelves.

Dr. Franklin smiled. "I have invented an arm-extender." He showed Noah how to use the invention to reach books near the ceiling. Holding the long handle, Noah asked, "Do you have a copy of my speller in your library?"

"Most certainly," Mr. Franklin replied. "My grandchildren are learning to read by using your blue-backed book. I've heard that your spellers are selling even better than my inventions. Your books are being printed and sold and read in every major American city." He nodded at Noah. "You are being called the schoolmaster of America." He walked to his desk and sat down. "I have even read in a Boston paper about your lectures."

"Thank you for your kind words, Dr. Franklin," Noah said. "I am happy to hear them."

The two men talked for hours about words and spelling. Benjamin Franklin suggested that all silent letters be left out of words.

Bread, head, give, and *friend* would be spelled *bred, hed, giv,* and *frend.*

"It sounds like a good idea," Noah said, "but it would be a big job to work it out."

"I think you could do it," Mr. Franklin said. "It would certainly help those who have trouble learning to spell."

"I'd like to," Noah agreed, "but right now, I'm looking for a job that pays enough to earn a living." He hesitated. "Writing is in my blood, but I can't earn enough with my writing to eat or rent a room." He walked toward the stairs. "I must leave now," Noah said. "It's been good to talk with you."

"Please come back again," Mr. Franklin said. "In fact, why don't you attend Christ Church with us this Sunday and then join us for dinner?"

"That is most kind of you," Noah said. "I'll be glad to come."

After he left, Noah remembered that he had forgotten to ask about the heated baths. *Perhaps I can do that on Sunday,* he thought. *What a fascinating gentleman is the witty Dr. Franklin. And to think that he has a copy of my speller in his library.*

Noah jumped on his horse and headed full gallop down Market Street toward his room. The warmth of this visit at Franklin Court would help him through the following months.

One evening, George Washington paid a call on Noah Webster. General Washington was in Philadelphia to help form the Constitution, and he had read Noah's book which first suggested the idea of a constitution.

"Come in, Mr. Washington," Noah cordially invited. The general entered Noah's small living quarters, placing his cape on a stool.

Young Mr. Webster was proud to receive such an important visitor as George Washington. Rumors were going around that Mr. Washington might be President of the newly formed country. Noah had admired the general ever since he first saw him in New Haven during the Revolutionary War.

"Mr. Webster, I have studied your book with great interest and want you to know that it has given me much food for thought."

Noah said nothing, waiting for the general to continue.

"You have a good head on you," Mr. Washington said. "We are using many of your ideas as we set up this new constitution."

"I love my country," Noah said. "I will do anything I can for it."

"Don't be surprised if people make fun of you," George Washington said. "Your ideas are ahead of their time, but some day people will respect them." With that, he picked up his cape, said good night to Noah, and went out into the dark.

People did laugh at Noah. They wrote untrue things about him. Making up a story about Noah, one writer said, "When Noah Webster came to Philadelphia, a friend met him and said, 'I congratulate you on your arrival to Philadelphia.'" "'Sir,'" Noah was supposed to have replied, "'you may congratulate Philadelphia because I am here.'" Many men and women thought Noah was too proud of himself.

Noah made many friends as well as enemies in Philadelphia. On the first day of March, he was invited to a gathering at the home of Mrs. Duncan Ingraham.

He walked to the splendid home and lifted the brass knocker at the door. A servant led him into the parlor.

"Mr. Webster, I'd like to have you meet my sister, Rebecca Greenleaf," Mrs. Ingraham said as he entered.

Noah looked down at a beautiful young lady. She was slender, with dark hair and sparkling brown eyes. His heart pounded. *I've met many lovely young ladies, but I never felt this way before.* It took a minute or two to get the courage to say anything.

"Good evening, Miss Greenleaf," he finally said. "I'm pleased to meet you."

The evening passed too quickly. When he went back to his room, Noah sat on the side of his bed and thought about what a wonderful night it had been. He took out his diary and wrote, "I met the sweet Miss Greenleaf this evening."

Three days later, in his diary, he called her "the agreeable Miss Greenleaf." By March twenty-second, she was "the lovely Becca."

Noah also met James Greenleaf, Rebecca's brother, who was also visiting the Ingrahams. Noah and James became good friends too.

During the mild spring evenings, Noah and Rebecca walked together and talked about their families. Noah told her about his parents and his brothers and sisters.

Rebecca told Noah that she was number thirteen out of fifteen children born to William and Mary Greenleaf. She told him about her brother John who was accidentally blinded by his brothers.

Noah was shocked. "How did that happen?"

Rebecca told the story. "When my brothers were small, the Revolutionary War was the main topic of conversation in Boston, where we lived. The boys would have mock fights, one side being the Colonists and the other side the

British. In one of their battles, one brother threw a paper dart at John and blinded him in one eye." She paused, then went on. "The next year, in just such another combat, using frozen turnips and apples as missiles, the sight of the other eye was destroyed."

Noah said, "It would be terrible to be without eyesight and not be able to read. I don't think I could stand it."

"I read the Bible to John for hours at a time," Becca said. "That's how I learned so many Scriptures."

One warm evening in June, Noah and Rebecca walked together down a garden path behind Becca's sister's house. A round yellow moon played hide-and-seek on their faces as it peeked through the branches of a maple tree. Noah smelled the roses blooming beside the path. Fireflies flitted like little lanterns everywhere.

"Mr. Webster, I must return to Boston this month," Rebecca said.

Noah gently pulled her down onto a bench beneath a rose arbor. "Please call me Noah, my dear Becca," he said.

"All right, Noah." She whispered softly, "I'll miss you."

"I will miss you too. I love you very much." Noah put his big hand over her small one. "May I ask your father for permission to marry you?" he asked.

He saw Rebecca look down at the small stones beneath their feet as she replied, "Yes, you may." Her eyes looked into his. "I would be honored to be your wife."

After Rebecca returned to Boston, Noah was lonely. He knew that he would have to get a dependable job before he could marry her. Rebecca was used to living in a fancy house with nice furniture and dishes. Her father had been a wealthy merchant before the Revolutionary War.

On October 16, 1787, Noah wrote in his diary: "My birthday. Twenty-nine years of my life gone!"

Noah Webster, the schoolteacher, writer, lawyer, and lecturer, now planned to move to New York City to become a magazine editor. In New York, Noah was even more lonesome for Rebecca. He sent her a lock of his reddish-brown hair so she wouldn't forget him. Naming his magazine *The American Magazine,* he put all his efforts into making it a success. After a year, he lost money on the project and it failed.

Noah wanted to get married, but Rebecca's father wrote and told him that Noah must have a job before he could marry his daughter. Rebecca's brother James also wrote and urged Noah to wait until he had more money before he married.

Noah decided to try being a lawyer again. He moved back to Hartford. Some money came

in from the sale of his books. In June, he wrote
to James, "I want to marry your sister as soon
as I get a house for us to live in. Could you lend
us some money?"

James Greenleaf gave Noah and Rebecca
$1,000 to buy furniture. Rebecca spent it all in
a short time, buying mirrors, china, and chairs.
They still had no pots and pans and no furniture for the parlor. Tearfully Rebecca confessed
to Noah that the money was gone. He gave her
$100 to buy her wedding dress. "We'll have
bare rooms for a while, but don't worry about it.
We have each other."

Noah and Rebecca were married on October
26, 1789, in her parents' home in Boston. She
was twenty-three, eight years younger than her
husband. Rebecca's sister Priscilla came to
stay with them in the large house in Hartford
which they rented for $100 a month.

Noah enjoyed eating Rebecca's pies and
puddings. He thought that she was happy too,
but one day, after Priscilla had returned home,
Noah found his wife crying in the parlor.

"What is wrong, my dear?" he asked.

"I'm so homesick," she cried. "I miss my
parents and my home in Boston." A flood of
tears came as she continued. "We had such
good times there." Looking at Noah, she said,
"You are so busy and gone so much of the time.
I'm so lonely."

Putting his arms around Rebecca, Noah said, "My dear little wife, I love you so much. Would it help if we invited some friends to come and visit?"

Soon, Rebecca was so busy entertaining that she didn't have time to be homesick. In early November, she wrote to her parents that she had baked eleven pumpkin puddings, three plum puddings, and seven apple pies. Noah began to gain weight from eating all the good desserts.

On Thanksgiving Day, the young Mr. and Mrs. Webster visited Noah's parents. Rebecca dressed up in her new green dress with pink and red roses on it. She put a ruffled bonnet on her head. Noah wore his new broadcloth suit, silk stockings, and silver-buckled shoes.

Noah's brothers and sisters and their children were home for the holiday. The children gathered around their new Aunt Becca in the parlor, admiring her dress and telling Noah how pretty she was.

When Ma took the turkey out of the brick oven, they all gathered around the tables which had been pushed together to make room for everyone. Noah looked around the room. He loved his family and was so proud that he could bring his new bride to be a part of this gathering!

Noah's father, Deacon Webster, prayed a prayer of thanksgiving as they held hands around the table. Noah held Becca's slim hand on his left and Ma's work-roughened fingers on his right.

After the prayer ended, Noah asked, "What do you think of our new President?"

"General Washington is a fine man," said Abram.

"Yes," Noah agreed, "You remember, don't you, that I stayed in his home in Mount Vernon and had dinner with him and his wife?" He spoke with pride. "He also came to see me in Philadelphia when he was there for the signing of the Constitution. He will make a great President."

"I think that too," said Pa. "He certainly had what it took to see us through the war."

"We pray for him every day," Ma added. "Leading our country will be a bigger job than leading the army."

After the big dinner, everyone told Ma what a delicious meal it was. She turned to Rebecca. "You're doing a good job feeding our Noah. He looks as fit as a fiddle."

Rebecca laughed. "He loves my cooking, but it can't match yours, Mother Webster."

With a pleased smile, Ma turned to Noah. "I'm glad you married Rebecca, son. She is a fine girl. Please bring her to see us often."

Noah put one arm around Rebecca and the other around his mother. "I'll do that, Ma. Thank you for the wonderful meal."

When they arrived home that evening, Noah headed for his desk. He was working on an article against slavery.

"Noah, you write day and night," Rebecca said. "Don't you get tired of studying and writing constantly? You'll wear out your eyes."

Noah paused so he could explain exactly how he felt. "Writing is as natural to me as breathing," he said. "I feel that I *must* write. There is so much that needs to be put into written words."

Rebecca went into the chamber shaking her head. Noah swiveled his chair and watched her leave. *I love my wife. But, like so many others, she doesn't understand that I have to write.* He sighed and picked up his goosequill pen once again.

11

The Family Man

August 1790

Years passed. In 1791, Noah published *The Prompter*. He thought of himself as the man who, in plays, sits behind the actors, correcting them when wrong and helping them remember when they forget. "I love my country," he said, "but I can see America's faults. I must do all that I can to help us go forward with spirit and correct our problems."

Noah and Rebecca's daughters, Emily and Julia, were born in Hartford. Noah's love for his children helped to ease the pain that he felt when his mother died in 1794.

Noah moved his family to New York City so that he could be a newspaper editor. A new baby, Harriet, was born here. After a short time in the city, the Websters located a house in the country. Noah always preferred rural life.

In 1798, the Websters moved back to Connecticut, to New Haven. They bought a large old-fashioned house on Water Street.

"Did you know that Benedict Arnold once lived in this house?" Noah asked his two older daughters.

"Who was Benedict Arnold, Papa?" asked dark-haired Emily, now eight years old.

"He was a traitor."

"What's a traitor?" little Julia asked, her brown eyes shining.

"It's someone who betrays his country to the enemy." Noah took his daughters by their hands and said, "Come with me. I'll show you something I found in the attic."

The two girls walked down the hall with their father past the kitchen, where Rebecca was preparing supper. She stood beside the broad fireplace, which could hold half a cord of wood at one time. Baby Harriet played on the floor.

"We're going to the attic, Mama," five-year-old Julia said. "Papa wants to show us what he found up there."

Noah and his daughters climbed the stairs to the second floor. They walked down another long hall and came to a locked door. By turning a large key, Noah opened the door to another stairway. As they climbed more stairs, Mr. Webster said, "Our new neighbors told me that Benedict Arnold smuggled goods into America without paying duty. It's said that he hid them up here in the attic."

When they reached the top of the stairs, the girls looked around the huge room. Two immense chimneys went through from floor to roof. Dormer windows let in light.

"This would be a nice play room," Emily said. "I'm going to bring my dolls up here."

"What did you want to show us, Papa?" asked Julia.

"Look at this," Noah said, as he picked up the scabbard of a sword.

"What is it?" the girls asked.

"It's the holder for a sword," Noah said. "I'm sure that it belonged to General Arnold."

The girls' eyes opened wide with wonder. "Can we play with it?"

"I don't know why not," Noah said. "It's our house now. You may play here anytime you wish."

The following year, baby Mary was born, the only child in the family with blond hair and blue eyes. Two years later, a son, William, arrived. When he was two years old, baby Eliza joined the family.

The older children went to a day school taught by Miss Eunice Hall, where they learned to read, write, spell, cipher, and sew.

When the great eclipse of 1806 occurred, the Webster children, having heard of it from their parents, carefully carried their pieces of smoked glass to school.

"Teacher, we brought this to protect our eyes while we see the eclipse," Emily said when they arrived.

Miss Hall took the pieces of glass from the girls. Closing the shutters over the windows, she took a bit of the glass in her hand. She held it to her eye for a few seconds. Taking it down, she said, "Oh, I would not have you see it for the world."

The teacher kept her pupils inside the dark room until the eclipse was over. Disappointed, the two Webster children arrived home to their parents too late to see anything.

Mr. Webster was so displeased that he removed his children from the school. "Such a teacher isn't fit to teach," he grumbled. "I can't imagine such ignorance."

Noah Webster and a group of leading citizens opened a new school. Called the Union

School, it was a brick building with two rooms, one for boys and one for girls. Noah was president of the school, which had an enrollment of fifty-two boys and sixty-three girls. Among the pupils were the two oldest Webster children.

Noah kept writing. One day he sat in his study over the parlor. He was forty-one years old. He was thinking, of all things, about the time he came down with smallpox when he was in college. Then he recalled how sick his own daughters had been with scarlet fever.

In front of him lay a letter written by his old friend, Oliver Wolcott. It told of the yellow fever epidemic in Philadelphia back in 1793 when people died by the thousands. So many were helpless at that time. Even the doctors didn't know what to do.

"Becca, please come here," Noah called. From his open door, he watched her run up the stairs.

"What is it, dear?" she gasped.

"Do you remember the high temperature and bright red rash the girls had with scarlet fever?"

"Of course I remember. How could I ever forget?" she said. "I was up with them all night for several nights. The vomiting was terrible. Do you remember how all the skin peeled off the ends of their fingers and toes?"

"Yes, I do," Noah said. "I believe I'll write a book to tell the things I've learned about diseases."

Rebecca smiled. "You are just the one to do it, Noah. You've studied about it for years. A book like that is certainly needed. And your other books are selling well." She turned to leave. "I'm going back downstairs. I'm fixing your favorite meal for this noon."

"Roast beef with applesauce?" asked Noah.

"Yes," said Rebecca. She put her arm around his shoulder. "You work too hard, Noah, but I love you just as you are."

Noah was pleased. He had already decided to write the book, but he needed to hear his wife say that it was a good idea. After Rebecca went down the stairs to her kitchen, Noah sat for awhile. *What a thoughtful wife I have.* Smiling, he took up his pen and began to write.

Mr. Webster liked this house on the water in New Haven. When he tired of writing, he could look across the Sound and see Long Island on a clear day.

The large garden out back kept him busy raising green beans and sweet corn for their summer meals. Many fruit trees grew in their orchard. Often Noah came in carrying a basket of apples or peaches, saying, "Now children, eat all the fruit you want."

When his work was done for the day, Noah walked along the elm-shaded streets of the city. Sometimes he went past Yale College and remembered his years as a student during the war.

In his diary he wrote, "On the fourteenth of December, 1799, died the Great and Good Washington in the sixty-eighth year of his age after twenty-four hour's illness. All America mourns."

Noah's thoughts traveled back to Yale, to Mount Vernon, and to Philadelphia. *A great leader and good friend is gone. I will miss George Washington.*

****

On June 4, 1800, Noah Webster put an announcement in the newspaper saying that he was writing a new dictionary. He felt that America needed a dictionary of its own. Many of the words in Samuel Johnson's British dictionary were unknown in this country.

At once, people began to make fun of his project.

"Who ever heard of writing a book about words?" one lady said.

"We already have Johnson's dictionary, printed in England. What's wrong with it?" a man asked.

"Mr. Webster's dictionary is another Noah's Ark," jeered an editor. "Instead of unclean animals in it, he has unclean words." The man was displeased because Noah planned to include American words such as *skunk* and *applesauce* and *bullfrog*, which were not in Dr. Johnson's dictionary. Mr. Webster thought of his old favorite Bible story. *That* Noah was ridiculed too, but he kept on building the ark. Noah Webster continued writing his dictionary.

Noah studied many languages so that he could find out where words came from. Soon he knew twenty languages. He knew more about medicine than many doctors of his day. Science was a hobby for him. His law books taught him about government. In all his travels and studies, he learned other interesting facts. All this helped in writing the dictionary.

The year 1806 was a sad one for Noah and Rebecca. A baby boy, Henry, born in November, died a few weeks later.

One happy day came when Noah's father, at the age of eighty-four, married Sara Hopkins of Hartford. This relieved Noah of the worry about his father living by himself. Two years later, a girl, Louisa, was born to Noah and Rebecca.

In April 1808, Noah's wife and daughters went to a revival meeting where Moses Stuart, pastor of the Congregational Center Church, preached. Night after night they attended the services.

"Please come with us, Father," his daughters pleaded. "We have all been converted. We're praying for you."

"No, I'm too busy tonight. I must keep writing. Perhaps some other time," he told them each time they asked him to go with them.

One evening, after the others left for church, Noah tried to study. He couldn't seem to keep the words in his mind. *What is wrong with me? I just can't seem to think straight.* He paced around the room. The ticking of the grandfather clock was the only noise in the quiet house. Sitting back at his desk, he decided that it was useless to read. He closed his books.

Pacing the floor again, his eyes were drawn to the shelf where the Bible lay. Picking it up, he sat down in the large chair beside his desk and opened the Bible. He read in 1 John 1:9, "If we confess our sins, he is faithful and just to forgive us our sins, and to cleanse us from all unrighteousness." *That's certainly plain enough. I need to confess, and God will forgive.*

Dropping to his knees, Noah began to pray. "Please forgive my sins. I ask You to forgive me and help me to be a true follower of Yours."

Giving his whole self to his Maker and Re-
deemer, Noah felt a great peace come to his
heart.

When his family returned from church, Noah met them at the door. "Rebecca. Children. I have good news for you."

Rebecca took one look at Noah's face and knew that her husband had met the Lord. Noah saw his joy reflected in her face as she realized that he had been converted. They rejoiced and praised God together.

That evening, Noah gathered his family around him. "I have failed as a father," he said. With his voice breaking, he continued. "I've neglected family prayer." He began at once to read the Scriptures and to lead his household in prayer.

From that day on, Noah wanted to do God's will. He prayed three times a day, asking that he and all of his family might live for God. "I believe that Christ is divine and that all the miracles of the Bible are true," he stated. Some of his friends criticized his new faith, but this only made Noah more determined to serve God.

In late April, Noah, with his daughters Emily and Julia, made a public profession of faith. Rebecca was ill that day and missed hearing Noah say, "Here am I with the children whom God has given me," as he stood before the congregation giving praise to his Lord. Twelve-year-old Harriet soon joined them in publicly proclaiming her faith.

"I believe I'll do a better job on the dictionary now," he told Rebecca one day as he sat at his long, half-circle table. "I have God to guide and direct me."

Spreading his books out, he worked from right to left, moving along in his swivel chair. He checked each word in the twenty different languages.

Some of the definitions in his dictionary showed his new beliefs. One was the word *love*. After the verb form, he wrote, "The Christian *loves* his Bible. If our hearts are right, we *love* God above all things." The noun form was similar: "The *love* of God is the first duty of man."

At four o'clock each day, Noah took a break from his writing. "Thank you, dear," he said to Rebecca, as she came in carrying a tray of fruit and cake.

"You work so hard, Noah," Becca said. "I wish you could take some time away from your dictionary."

"I enjoy studying," Noah said. "It's my play as well as my work." He rubbed his eyes. "My eyes do hurt, though, from all the reading. Call the children. We'll go out to the garden."

Gathering his children around him outside, Noah picked a tulip and pointed out its beauty.

"Your Heavenly Father made everything beautiful to make us happy," he said. "Don't ever forget that this is God's world. He created it for our enjoyment, and we are to take care of it the best we can."

Years went by. Trouble was brewing between England and the United States. Soon the War of 1812 would disrupt the peace.

Prices were high. Food and other products were scarce. Noah decided to move with his wife and seven children to Amherst, Massachusetts, in the foothills of the Green Mountains.

Emily and Julia, the two older girls, were engaged to be married and didn't want to leave New Haven. "Why do we have to move, Father?" they asked. "No one will know where we are in that little village."

"We can live cheaper in Amherst," Noah replied. "The country life will be good for us all. We'll go up by stagecoach and I'll show you the town."

The next day, the Websters boarded a coach and went north. After an overnight stop in Hartford at a small hotel, the stagecoach rolled slowly through the South Hadley woods. Overarching tree branches made a canopy above. The five younger children reached up and touched the branches as they went along. Emily and Julia sat quietly weeping as they thought of their lovers left behind.

Arriving in Amherst, the Websters found a village of about twenty-five small houses with three or four larger homes. One street ran north and south, the other east and west. The common, where each family was allowed to pasture a cow for several weeks a season, was a swamp of white birch and pasture land.

"Let's go first and visit my minister friend, Dr. David Parsons," Mr. Webster said. "Perhaps he will help us locate a house."

Rebecca gazed at the lovely hills and forests. Looking to the west, she could see the Connecticut River, about eight miles away. In the distance were the Green Mountains of Vermont.

"I believe we will all be happy here in such a beautiful place," she said. "Truly, God has led us here."

Noah located a large house on a hillside opposite the village green. Ten acres of meadowland surrounded it. They bought it and, after a trip back to New Haven, moved in.

Noah planted vineyards and orchards of apples, pears, peaches, and cherries. He raised all the family's vegetables. Noah liked farming. "I feel like I'm back where I belong," he told his family.

A pig named Heliogabalus lived in the pig pen. Three cows, Gentle, Comfort, and Cricket, roamed in the pasture. Mary Webster named her father's horse Rolla after she read a play about the conquest of Mexico.

Emily and Julia were happy now. Their friends from New Haven came to see them in Amherst. Noah and his three oldest daughters started a choir in the First Congregational Church. They attended all the Sunday services and revival meetings on week nights. Mr. Webster organized a Sunday school in the church.

The Webster children played with the Parsons children. Emily Webster and Harriet Parsons were best friends. They read books together. With their brothers and sisters, they acted out plays to entertain their families.

One Friday evening after the Webster and Parsons families had finished their supper, three ministers came riding over the hills, planning to eat with Dr. Parsons. Nothing was ready for the unexpected company. All the food was gone. With the fire out, there was no way that Mrs. Parsons could bake in her Dutch oven.

Dr. Parsons invited the men to make a call on his neighbor, Mr. Noah Webster. Escorting the ministers across the green, he was met by Rebecca. She immediately realized the problem.

"I'm all ready for them," she said. "My daughters and I baked in the big oven today."

Noah led the clergymen to a full table with roast ham and chickens, baked beans, bread, and pies of all sorts. By the glow of candlelight, Noah looked at the scene. His thoughts went back to Mount Vernon. Remembering the generosity of George and Martha Washington to a tired, hungry young man, Noah looked at his wife. *She is made of the same stuff,* he thought.

"My dear wife, you are a jewel," he told Rebecca that evening as they prepared for bed. "I never cease to be amazed at your hospitality. Your doors are open as wide as your heart."

12
The Dictionary

November 1813

Word came that Noah's father had died. He was ninety-one. Noah went to his room and sat for a long time with his head bowed. *I owe my father so much. If he hadn't sacrificed to send me to college, I wouldn't be here today working on this dictionary.*

Year after year, Noah worked on his project. His study was upstairs in a room overlooking the hills that surrounded Amherst. The walls were lined with books. Each day he rose at daybreak and went to his study for prayer as soon as he was dressed. In about half an hour, he walked outside the children's rooms calling, "Up, up, children!"

When everyone was gathered in the parlor, Noah led in prayer. After reading the Scriptures, the family ate breakfast together. When the meal was done, Noah grabbed a handful of raisins and went back to his study.

In his large room, Noah worked at the long table. Dictionaries and grammars of all languages lay in order. Noah would take the word he was working with and look it up in a dictionary. Making notes, he went to a grammar, then to a dictionary of another language. He worked his way around the table many times during a day's work.

As busy as Noah was with his writing and farming, he still took time to help start Amherst College. In 1820, he became President of the Board of Trustees. During this time, his only income came from the sales of the little blue-backed speller.

The three older girls, Emily, Julia, and Harriet, married and moved away. Mary, everyone's favorite, was a cheerful girl with blue eyes, long dark lashes and thick, light brown hair. She loved poetry. The minister, Dr. Parsons, said she sang like an angel. Noah liked to read his speeches and writings to Mary. She listened and made helpful suggestions.

When Mary was nineteen, she married a widower, Horatio Southgate, who had three children. They moved to Portland, Maine. A year later, a baby girl was born. The baby was named Mary, after her mother. The good news came to Amherst by mail.

A few weeks later, the mail brought bad news to the Websters. Opening the letter in the parlor, Noah immediately left the room. Mrs. Webster followed him. He was in his study, weeping.

"What is wrong, Noah?" Rebecca asked.

"Oh, Becca, our daughter is gone," he cried.

Rebecca came over and sat by him. "What do you mean?"

"Read this," Noah said, handing her the letter.

Rebecca read the words and began to cry. "Oh no," she sobbed. "Our beautiful Mary is dead. Only twenty years old, and dead." She looked at the date on the letter. "She is being buried today."

"The mail must have been delayed by the snowstorm we just had," Noah said. His voice broke. "Let's pray."

Noah and Rebecca knelt beside the chair and asked God for comfort. After a time of prayer, they went to tell the sad news to the other children.

Another sorrow came. Harriet's husband and baby died. When this happened, Harriet, at the age of twenty-one, came home to live. Little Louise, Noah and Rebecca's youngest girl, then became very ill and was left mentally retarded. Only their strong faith in God carried Noah and his family through these tragic events.

Noah and Rebecca adopted their little granddaughter, Mary Southgate. At the age of two, she came to live with them. They loved her as much as their own children. She helped to fill the empty spot in Noah and Rebecca's heart.

Mr. Webster disliked idleness. Seeing a boy loitering along the streets, he would ask, "Are you busy?" If the boy was not doing anything, Noah said, "Go work in my garden for an hour," or "Pick up the stones from the road in front of my house." He then paid the boy a silver ninepence an hour, a generous wage for a boy of that period.

The boys liked Mr. Webster and went by his house on purpose to be hired. He taught them about plants and budding and explained how to graft fruit trees.

One day, when Rebecca brought the usual four o'clock treats, Noah asked her to stay a few minutes.

Taking a piece of chocolate cake off the tray, Noah said, "I'm behind on my dictionary work. I've only reached the letter *H*. I need to be close to a large library so that I can look up information about words."

"Your spelling books are selling well," Rebecca said. "Perhaps we should move to a larger city."

"I've been thinking of going to either Boston or New Haven." Noah turned toward his wife. "Which do you prefer?"

"I believe New Haven would be better," Rebecca said. "Julia lives there and Emily is nearby in Hartford. And we have many friends in New Haven."

Noah was happy that his wife agreed with him. "We can afford to move now," he said. "Let's start packing."

Mr. Webster hired David Hoadley to build a new house for $3,400. While it was being built on the corner of Temple and Grove streets, Noah, Rebecca, Harriet, Eliza, William, Louisa, and little Mary lived in a rented house for a year. It was great fun to plan the new house and to watch the progress as it went up.

First a cellar was dug; then the first and second floors were added. Twenty-three big windows were put in place. Stone steps and a portico were made in front of the house. The giant chimneys were built.

Finally, the last brush of white paint was dry and the green shutters were installed beside each window.

Noah and his family sewed the parlor carpet themselves. The day came when they carried it in and put it in place. Walking down the long hall from front to back door, they looked in each room. Parlor. Drawing room. Dining room. Kitchen. Two bedrooms. Upstairs were four more bedrooms and Noah's study. It was beautiful.

That evening the family gathered in the drawing room. At one side of the fireplace, beside a small bookcase, Noah sat in his large armchair. Rebecca was by the window in her sewing chair. The children sat on the sofa and on footstools. A portrait of General Washington looked down on the group. After reading from the Bible, Mr. Webster prayed, "We thank you, God, for this new home. Bless it and keep us ever true to you. In Jesus' Name. Amen."

At Christmas, the family decorated the porch with evergreens wrapped around the pillars beside the front steps. Wreaths hung at the windows. A huge Christmas tree with lighted candles welcomed the many visitors who came to the Webster parties. Julia, who lived nearby, popped in and out several times a day.

Yale College honored Noah Webster with an honorary Doctor of Laws degree in 1823. More years went by. Noah worked on his dictionary until four every afternoon. He had already spent nearly $25,000 on the project. "I'd like to visit Europe and study in the big libraries there," he said. "But after building a new house, I have no money left."

One day, Harriet came to Noah with her hand extended. "Here is something to help you, Father." Noah looked at the money she gave him. It was $1,000, taken from her savings.

"Are you sure that you want to do this, Harriet?" Noah asked.

"Yes. I believe in what you are doing," Harriet said. "The dictionary is important to our country. Please take the money. If you can pay it back, all right. If not, consider it a gift from your daughter."

Noah accepted the money with gratitude and made plans to leave. After praying with his family, he boarded ship. His twenty-two-year-old son, William, went with him. They sailed from New York City in June 1824.

Three days out on the sea, they ran into a terrible storm. The ocean rolled and foamed. Noah enjoyed watching the gigantic waves, but William was seasick. He lay in his berth day and night. To cheer him, Noah told him of seeing a canary on board, in a cage, hanging over the gangway of the ship. At the height of the storm, in the midst of the roaring sea, the little bird cheered them all with her beautiful song. "Just as that little bird has complete trust, so we can trust in our Heavenly Father to bring us safely across the ocean," Noah said.

They reached France in three weeks. Taking a steamboat up the Seine River, they saw houses built of stone with steep roofs covered with thatch, or straw. Villages with narrow streets only six feet wide lined the riverbank.

The following day, Noah and William rode in a coach driven by six horses. They arrived in Paris that evening. After locating a two-room apartment, Noah went to see the Royal Library. What a thrill! Rows upon rows of shelves thirty feet high, all filled with books, lined the walls.

Mr. Webster arose at six every morning. He dressed in his black coat, black silk stockings, and buckled shoes. After two or three hours of writing, he ate breakfast and then went to the library. William spent the time learning to speak and write French.

Dinner was at five o'clock. "This food is terrible," Noah complained to William, as they ate in a sidewalk cafe. "I miss your Mother's roast beef with gravy."

"I agree," William said, "and this French bread doesn't hold a candle to her biscuits."

Noah wrote to Rebecca, "I miss my tea. Most of the French drink wine at breakfast and dinner. The butter is unsalted. People salt it as they use it, on bread." He went on, "The bread comes in long loaves, about two and a half feet long, almost all crust. I'll be glad to get back to American food."

Each night Noah and his son took a walk, visiting famous places. While they were still in France, Harriet wrote that she had purchased a piano, was taking lessons, and was engaged to marry William Fowler. Noah was glad to hear the good news.

After three months in Paris, Noah and William boarded a steamboat and arrived in England thirteen hours later. In Cambridge, they rented a furnished three-room apartment with two bedrooms and a fireplace. Noah wrote to his family in America, "It's a pleasure to be among people that look, dress, eat, cook, and talk like our own people.

From Connecticut, Rebecca wrote about harvesting the garden, drying corn and beans for succotash, and putting beets in the cellar. The wood was in the shed. She was working on a third bedquilt, with all the winter clothing made.

In another letter, Rebecca told about the excitement of meeting General Lafayette from France. Handbills were passed out informing the residents that the general was arriving at ten that evening. Every family in New Haven was asked to put candles in the windows of their houses to welcome him.

Rebecca and her daughters made potato candlesticks and put their candles on the window sills. When the gun was fired, announcing the arrival of the general, every house was lighted. Rebecca and Harriet walked around the green to see the sight. The next day, they met General Lafayette in person at the college library.

In January 1825, Noah came to the last page of his book. His hand began to shake so badly that he couldn't hold his pen steady. He wrote the last word.

"Help me walk a bit, William," he said. "I'm trembling." As Noah walked around the room, he recovered his strength.

"You have reason to be tired," William said. "You've worked on this dictionary for twenty-five years and have written definitions for 70,000 words. All done by hand."

Noah and William spent day after day looking for a publisher. No one in England was interested. Discouraged, they came home to New Haven in June.

In America, word had spread about the new dictionary. People were excited. No longer ridiculed, Noah Webster received a hero's welcome. Everywhere he went he was honored. Family and friends were happy to see him again.

Shortly after Noah's return, he attended the weddings of both Harriet and Eliza. Then he started looking for someone who would publish the dictionary. At last he found a printer to do the job. On his seventieth birthday, October 16, 1828, Noah turned to Rebecca and took her small hand in his. "Let us give thanks to God for helping us complete this great work," he said. Together they knelt and gave God praise for His guidance and wisdom.

The dictionary was very popular. It was printed in two volumes and sold for twenty dollars. The first 2,500 copies sold out and more were printed. It soon became the standard in England as well as in America. With a copy which he sent to Queen Victoria, Noah added a note, "Our common language is one of the ties that bind our two nations together."

Noah spent his final years in the peaceful home in New Haven.

He loved his family. "It's lonely around here with the children gone," Noah said, as he sat in his rocking chair one evening.

"I know, dear," Rebecca said, "but we have many friends, and God has blessed us with a wonderful family."

"Yes, that's true," Noah replied, "but I need to keep busy. I think I'll write more books for school children."

Rebecca shook her head and smiled, "Yes, you might as well. You would be unhappy if you weren't writing."

Noah began his next project. Seven more books were written for the children of America to use in their school rooms.

Visitors came often to the Webster home now that Dr. Noah Webster was famous. At age eighty, Noah's hair was thinner and getting gray. He was heavier and walked more slowly but still kept up with people who were much younger.

Noah enjoyed his grandchildren. Their visits were the highlight of his day. "Have a peppermint," he told them, as he reached into the bag filled with candy. Climbing on his lap, they searched his pockets for the raisins he always kept there.

Grandpa Webster scolded the youngsters if they used bad words. "I have never used bad language," he said. "It hurts me to hear you swear. Don't ever do it again." One little granddaughter, when she heard him scold her cousin for swearing, said, "Grandfather makes me shiver like a top."

When Noah was asked the secret of his long life, he replied, "I have always gone to bed early and got up with the birds." A thoughtful look came over his face as he said, "I worked hard and enjoyed it." Noah *was* a hard worker. Words were his livelihood and, next to his family, his greatest joy.

One evening, Mrs. Webster heard someone talking in the drawing room. She looked in. Noah stood in front of the pictures of his children, talking to them.

"What are you doing, Noah?" she asked.

"Oh, Becca, I miss our children and grandchildren. I was just telling them how much I love them."

The grandfather clock struck nine. Noah looked up. "I wonder what each one is doing right now?" he said.

"They're probably going to bed," said Rebecca. "And so are you," she added, as she took him by the hand and gently led him upstairs.

On Noah and Rebecca's fiftieth wedding anniversary, all the children, grandchildren, and great-grandchildren gathered at the Webster home to help them celebrate. Thirty-five sat around the table at dinner.

"This is the happiest day of my life," Noah said, after they prayed together that evening. He looked around the room. "I have something for each of you." With love shining from his eyes, he gave each one a copy of his translation of the Bible. He signed his name in each copy. This was the last gift he ever gave.

Sunday, May 21, 1843, Mr. Webster went to church as usual. On Monday, he walked to the post office twice. When he got home, he felt chilled. By Friday he had a fever. The following Sunday he was critically ill.

Noah insisted on sleeping in his study so that he didn't bother Rebecca with his restlessness. As he became sicker, the family gathered around his bedside. Julia and Emily wept as their father waved his handkerchief before him and asked if Louisa was present. His concern for his retarded daughter was always on his mind. Rebecca, sitting with her hand in his, told him that all the family was there except one daughter who was away.

Many visitors came to see Noah as he was dying. The president of Yale College was there. Other friends came. Moses Stuart, the minister who had joyfully welcomed Noah into the family of God many years before, arrived.

"Are you ready to go, Mr. Webster?" he asked.

Noah opened his eyes. "I am ready," he whispered. "My work is all done. I know in whom I have believed. I am entirely submissive to the will of God."

Noah Webster died peacefully that evening. He was eighty-four. They buried his body in the Grove Street Cemetery in New Haven, just around the corner from his home. But his spirit went to be with his Savior whom he loved and served for thirty-five years.

After Noah died, Rebecca stayed on in the big house with Louisa and her maid, Lucy Griffin, a black lady who was an excellent cook and helper.

One day, Rebecca was hanging curtains in the parlor. The stool on which she was standing slipped, and she crashed to the floor. Rebecca screamed, "Lucy, help. I can't move."

Lucy came running. "What happened, Mistress Webster?"

Rebecca groaned. "I fell. Please go get the doctor."

Lucy ran out the door and raced up the street to the doctor's house. Panting, she shouted, "Come quick, Doctor Green. Mistress Webster fell. She's hurt real bad."

The doctor grabbed his black bag and ran back down the street with Lucy. Up the porch steps and into the parlor he hurried. After examining Rebecca, the doctor didn't give much hope. "She'll be paralyzed for the rest of her life if she lives," he said.

Rebecca never walked again, but she remained cheerful as ever. Her friends and family loved to come to visit her. Rebecca's daughters and Lucy cared for her until she died June 25, 1847.

****

After Noah's death, his speller and dictionary became even more popular. Printed in one volume, with the price down to six dollars, millions of copies of the dictionary were sold.

New dictionaries have been written as the years have gone by, but the one by Noah Webster is known as the finest book of its kind in the English language.

The man who loved words lives on in everyone's vocabulary. "Look it up in Webster" is said when people want the meaning of a new word. "According to Webster" shows where they got their information. The name *Webster* now means *dictionary*.

If Noah could return to earth today, he would find thousands of new words in use. *Automobile, radio, airplane, electricity, telephone, atomic energy, stereo, television, computer,* and many other words, would be unknown to him. But, being Noah Webster, it wouldn't be long before he would be looking up the meaning of each word and carefully writing it down.

A

allegory: A story told about fictional persons or events to teach or illustrate a moral principle.

almanack: (Former spelling of *almanac*) A yearly calendar giving the days, weeks, and months of the year, weather forecasts, astronomical information, and other information.

anvil: A heavy block of iron on which metal may be forged.

B

bachelor of arts: A degree given by a college or university to a person who has completed a four-year course of study.

basin: A round, open container used for holding water and other liquids.

bedchamber: A bedroom.

bellows: An instrument with an air chamber and flexible sides, used for blowing fires.

blacksmith: One who shoes horses and works iron on an anvil using a forge, hammer, and tongs.

Boston massacre: An incident in Boston in 1770 in which British troops killed three colonials.

Boston tea party: An uprising in Boston on December 16, 1773, against the British customs officials. Colonists, disguised as Indians, boarded the British ships in the harbor and dumped chests of tea overboard.

breeches: Colonial name for men's and boys' trousers.

broadcloth: A fine woolen cloth.

buttery: A place in a college from which students may get bread, butter, and drinks.

C

calico: Cheap cotton cloth printed in a figured pattern of bright colors.

census: An official count of the people of a country or district.

charter: An official document which gave the colony the right to rule itself.

churn: A vessel in which milk or cream is beaten vigorously to make butter.

ciphering: The colonial term for working out mathematics problems.

clapboard: A narrow board with one edge thinner than the other, nailed overlapping as siding on frame buildings.

cocked hat: A hat with the brim turned up in three places.

cockleburs: Coarse, branching weeds having burs about an inch long.

colonies: The British colonies that became the original states of the United States were New Hampshire, Massachusetts, Rhode Island, Connecticut, New York, New Jersey, Pennsylvania, Delaware, Maryland, Virginia, North Carolina, South Carolina, and Georgia.

common: A tract of land considered the property of the community, open to the use of all.

contagious: Spread by contact, as a disease.

continental: Pertaining to the thirteen American colonies during and just after the Revolution.

copyright: The exclusive right to publish one's written work.

cord: A measure for firewood, equaling a pile 4 x 4 x 8 feet, or 128 cubic feet.

crane: The metal arm by which pots were hung over the fire.

cutter: A small sleigh pulled by a horse.

D

deacon: A layperson who assists the minister.

doctor of laws: An advanced degree given by a college or university to a person who has completed a course of graduate study. It is sometimes given in recognition of great achievement, as in the case of Noah Webster.

dormitory: A building providing sleeping and living quarters, especially at a school or college.

E

eclipse: The passage of the moon between the sun and the observer.

esquire: A title of courtesy or respect.

F

featherbed: A mattress of strong fabric stuffed with feathers.

fife: A small, shrill-toned flute used mainly for military music.

flax: A blue-flowered plant with a slender stem which provides the fiber used in making linen.

foot stoves: A small metal box containing coals. Holes in the sides let the heat out for use in church, sleighs, and stagecoaches.

forge: A hearth or furnace where metals are heated and shaped.

fossils: The actual remains of plants or animals preserved in rocks.

G

gait: One of the ways in which a horse steps or runs.

garret: The colonial term for attic.

goosequill: The type of pen used by Noah Webster. It was made from the hollow, horny stem of a goose feather.

grammar: The study of language.

gristmill: A mill for grinding grain.

H

hitching post: A post to which a horse may be hitched.

horse block: A block or platform used in getting on or off a horse.

hulls: The outer covering of nuts.

husking bee: A corn-husking party.

I

import: To bring in goods from a foreign country for trade or sale.

injun pudding: Slang for Indian pudding, which was broth with cornmeal in it.

J

johnnycakes: Flat cakes made of cornmeal and baked on a griddle.

L

Latin: The language of ancient Rome. Much of our English language has Latin roots.

lectures: Speeches on specific subjects delivered to an audience.

linen: A fabric woven from the fibers of flax.

loom: A machine on which thread or yarn is woven into fabric.

M

major: In the military, an officer ranking next above a captain and next below a lieutenant colonel.

master of arts: A degree given by a college or university to a person who has completed a course of graduate study.

meetinghouse: A place of worship.

militia: A group of citizens trained in military organizations other than the regular military forces and called out only in emergencies.

muffler: A heavy scarf worn about the neck for warmth.

N

nine-pence: A unit of British money, the sum of nine pennies, worth about 12 cents in the 1800s in the United States.

P

parsonage: A minister's home, often provided by the church.

peel: A long-handled shovel used to move bread or other baked goods about in an oven.

pewter: A dull gray metal, usually made of tin and lead, used in making tableware in colonial days.

piazza: A veranda or porch.

pincers: An instrument having two handles and a pair of jaws used to pull teeth in colonial days.

pitchfork: A large fork with which to handle hay, straw, etc.

portico: A porch with a roof supported by columns.

primer: A beginning reading book.

privy: A small toilet or outhouse.

proverb: A brief saying that illustrates a truth.

R

redcoat: A British soldier during the American Revolution and the War of 1812, when a red coat was part of the uniform.

reins: Straps attached to the bit to control a horse.

representation: The system of electing delegates to act for the people who elect them.

Revolutionary War: The American war for independence from England (1775–1783).

rickety: Ready to fall, tottering.

ruddy: Having a healthy reddish glow.

rye: A hardy cereal grass, much like wheat.

S

sabbath: The Lord's Day. It may refer to either the first or the seventh day of the week, a day of rest and worship.

sad iron: An iron for pressing clothes, pointed at both ends, sometimes having a removable handle.

saddle bags: A pair of pouches connected by a strap or band and slung over an animal's back or attached to a saddle.

sanctuary: The part of a church where the altar is located.

scabbard: A case to hold the blade of a sword.

scabs: Crusts formed on the surface of a sore.

scarlet fever: A disease with fever and rash followed by scaling of the skin.

sconce: A wall bracket for holding a candle.

shaver: Colonial slang for a young boy.

shilling: A unit of British money used in England and the colonies, varying in value.

sloth: Not wanting to work, laziness.

smallpox: A highly contagious disease caused by a virus. Symptoms are a high temperature and blisters. It often leaves scars.

smudge pots: Containers for burning smoky fuels to produce a smudge; used to drive insects away in Noah's day.

soot: A black substance from incompletely burned wood or coal which settles inside chimneys and other surfaces in contact with smoke.

spectacles: A pair of eyeglasses.

spelling bee: A gathering at which contestants spell words. Those who misspell words are out of the competition.

spinning wheel: A device used for spinning yarn or thread.

spit: A pointed rod on which meat is turned and roasted before a fire.

stagecoach: A large, horse-drawn, four-wheeled vehicle having a regular route from town to town.

stagnant: Standing still, not flowing.

stone boat: A low, flat sled used for transporting rocks and other heavy objects.

sumac: A root-climbing plant which turns red in the fall.

symbolic: Expressed by symbols, as "The oak is symbolic of strength."

T

trundle bed: A bed with a very low frame so that it may be stored under another bed.

trustees: A body of men who hold the property and manage the affairs of a church, college, or other institution.

tunic: A garment with or without sleeves, reaching to the knees, usually worn without a belt.

typhoid fever: A disease caused by typhoid bacteria. Symptoms are fever, sick stomach, rash, and weakness.

U   V   W   Y

upperclassman: A junior or senior in a school or college.

vocal: Having to do with the voice.

waistcoat: A vest.

War of 1812: A war between the United States and England from 1812–1815.

warming pan: A closed metal pan with a long handle, containing hot coals for warming a bed.

whig: An American colonist who supported the Revolutionary War in the eighteenth century.

whist: A game of cards.

yellow fever: A disease caused by a virus transmitted by mosquitoes. Symptoms are bleeding, vomiting, and yellowing of the skin.